# GOLD FINDING

# $ECRETS

By
EDWIN P. MORGAN
California Historian

Dedicated to
Dr. Rockwell D. Hunt
"Mr. California"

FIFTH EDITION

Primitive methods of early days; pan, rocker and arrastra. Ernest Narjot, artist (?). Photo by courtesy of California Division of Mines and Geology.

Author's Photo

This old rocker was on exhibit in West Berlin July 24-August 8, 1965 during the Volks Fest. Property of the author.

# About The Author

By C. L. Johnson

## EDWIN P. MORGAN

Mr. Edwin P. Morgan, California historian and teacher, was born in the City of Oakland in 1914. He began prospecting and placer mining in the 1930's; first, in the Trinity Alps area, and later along the length of the Mother Lode.

He received professional help from an old-time GOLD miner and in this book is attempting to pass these secrets on to you. He has found GOLD prospecting enjoyable, though he never became rich. Because of the renewed interest of many people in seeking GOLD in California for pleasure, Mr. Morgan has written this book as a guide for them.

GOLD mining during the 1930's at Cow Creek on the Trinity River. Here I used first one then three sluice boxes, letting Cow Creek waters wash by ground sluicing the earth through the sluice boxes.

Open pit and surface sluicing appears more to my liking. One try at hard rock tunneling was enough for me.

# Foreword

This book has been written to help you search for your "pot of GOLD" at the end of the rainbow. It was designed as a personal guide to give you hidden secrets of the trade. Many guides have been written for the prospector, miner and amateur, but few really answer the questions you want to ask.

I believe you, the amateur, want to know where to find GOLD, how to recognize it when you find it, then how to recover the GOLD, and, of course, how to sell it.

First, in order to find GOLD, you should know where GOLD is located and how it got there. A short lesson in elementary geology and geography will help. Everyone says that GOLD is where you find it, and this is true. But no one is going to tell you where to find a bonanza, because if they knew where one was, they would have mined it themselves.

If you read this book carefully and use it as a personal guide, no doubt you will find GOLD. How much is difficult to say. You probably won't make a fortune, but a bonanza is not impossible. This is mainly written for the recreation miner who wants the fun of seeking GOLD for pleasure. If it becomes a profit—better yet. This book tells how to recognize GOLD, how to test it, and describes the placer mining equipment needed and how to make some of it.

Read this book and try your luck some weekend or vacation.

# Contents

# Acknowledgments

The author of this book appreciates the assistance received from:

John E. Morgan—Historical Research, Sacramento.

Walter Staley—Photography, Sacramento.

The Staff of the Bancroft Library, University of California.

The Staff of the California State Library, California Room.

Elisabeth L. Egenhoff and the staffs of the California Division of Mines and Geology, San Francisco and Sacramento, California. A special note of thanks for their contributions in photographs and drawings.

The kind assistance and information on laws and mining equipment and nugget discoveries:

The California Department of Fish and Game.

The California Division of Forestry.

The California State Beaches and Parks.

The California Water Pollution Board.

The United States Corp. of Engineers.

The United States Department of Interior, Land Office.

Also the many miners that have contributed help since the 1930's throughout the State of California.

A list of further reading sources will be found at the back of this book.

# Introducing Gold

**GOLD** is a magic word echoing down through history. It represented wealth even in the early centuries of the Christian era, and the idea of making GOLD from baser metals probably arose among the Alexandrian Greeks. Their fundamental theories were probably the beginning of chemistry and the preparation of medicines. Much later the luring tales of easy wealth brought thousands of 49'ers to the "GOLDEN STATE"—California.

What is this GOLD? Webster says, "It is a precious metal of bright yellow color." The color varies from pale white to golden yellow, and it is neither the rarest nor the most valuable metal.

"It is the most ductile (capable of being stretched) and malleable of all metals." A single gram of pure GOLD has been drawn into a wire two miles long! GOLD is 2.5 to 3 in hardness, on a scale of 10, which makes it a soft malleable metal, but it will become brittle if alloyed with too much silver, lead or cadmium.

"GOLD is one of the heaviest metals." Its atomic weight is 197.2. Pure 24-carat GOLD has a specific gravity of about 19.3, and weighs about 1,187 pounds per cubic foot. Because of the heavy weight, GOLD always settles to the bottom of your equipment or to bedrock.

"It is a symbol of wealth." Because of this, it is the foundation of world trade and commerce.

In science GOLD is element Au which forms into isometric crystals of GOLD, but the crystals are sometimes distorted into leaf-like shapes. It will melt at 1063° C.

How to test GOLD. For the amateur prospector, the easiest and most well-known method is to hammer it. GOLD, being soft, will flatten out when hammered. Also, a knife will cut into GOLD while pyrite (or Fool's Gold) will shatter. GOLD will not be affected by any single acid.

On April 23, 1965, Governor Edmund G. Brown signed SB 265 designating native GOLD as California's official State Mineral.

The State Motto "Eureka" means "I have found it" and refers to GOLD discovery.

# Gold Geology

Three billion years ago our planet Earth was nothing but a huge ball of fire, orbiting with eight other planets around the sun. Contained in this firey mass were many elements or basic building blocks. After five hundred million years passed, the cooling earth began to form a crust, locking in a great amount of heat and many of the elements. This period of time is known as the Pre-Cambrian era. Soon the heat reached such intensity as to melt the rocks on the bottom of the crust, and through this weak spot, great streams of molten magma (lava) would explode out upon the earth's surface, thus forming a new crust. This volcanic action took place many times during the earth's beginning.

Now let us advance the geologic time clock to a mere 180 million years ago, to the last great mountain building (mesozoic) era. This is when the present Sierra Nevada mountains were born. The mesozic era is divided into an early part, the triassic, followed by the jurassic, and finally the cretaceous periods. During the jurassic period many of man's valuable metals and precious jewels resulted. Most of the GOLD-bearing quartz veins in California are associated with the late jurassic plutonic rocks of the Sierra Nevada and Klamath Mountains.

Violent volcanic activity unlocked many trapped elements, such as Au (GOLD), from deep within the earth's core. These elements joined the magma which consisted of melted rock, minerals, and a considerable amount of water, and was erupted up through cracks to the surface crust. As the magma cooled and hardened, the water was expelled, carrying the minerals and elements into surface fissures or mineral and quartz veins. As the water evaporated. the minerals and GOLD formed into crystals, but many took the shape of the vein. When hard, these veins became lodes (example: California's Mother Lode). In some rare cases many minerals and elements formed together in these lodes causing a condition known as "rebellious" GOLD.

Near the end of this violent era, the Sierra Nevada folded, twisted and tipped. Then the volcanic activity quieted down as the present cenozoic (Greek for "Recent Life") era began. The cenozoic is divided into the tertiary (ter'shi-a-ri) period with its five subdivisions, called "epochs," and the quaternary (kwa-ter'na-ri) period. During the early tertiary period erosion took place, and laid bare the upper, richer parts of the GOLD-bearing veins, which resulted in releasing, removing, depositing and concentrating the GOLD into rich placer deposits. These deposits formed in ancient tertiary channels (or early north-south rivers). In these deposits are found GOLD from large lumps (called nuggets) to flakes, grains and dust. Later these tertiary channels became covered with more lava, and some were raised to mountain tops as the mountains tipped westward.

# Gold Geology

Leaving the tertiary period, we come to the last period, the quaternary. Due to shifting of the earth's surface, rivers started running westward, cutting through the ancient tertiary channels and residual placer deposits. These quaternary streams transported the placer GOLD down to the sea—or until natural riffles such as pot-holes, cracks, crevices or even bends in the stream stopped the GOLD and it sank to bedrock.

This brings us to the coming of man. To discover how man recovered this GOLD, read the history of mining near the end of the book.

Author's Photo

### TERTIARY RIVER BED
"Ancient lost tertiary river bed containing Free Placer Gold"

# Where To Look For Gold

It has been said many times, "GOLD is where you find it", and GOLD has been found in nearly every county of California; but in some areas it amounted to millions of dollars while in others, only a few dollars. Many places that had such large production of GOLD still offer possibilities for adventuring amateur prospectors. Mountain streams still carry new GOLD down each winter and leave both sand and gravel bars where one may explore.

But, do not forget that GOLD may be found other places than in streams. For the amateur miner, placer deposits are best. These are auriferous deposits that have been moved to lower elevations and contain free GOLD. Placer mining is carried on in the flat lands, hill and mountain sides, streams and rivers, gullies, ravines, canyons and alluvial slopes. Floods through the centuries have spread GOLD and silt across the land, both in thick and thin layers ranging from deposits hundreds of feet deep to those on the surface. Remember GOLD may be found anywhere, but that in certain places you stand a better chance of finding it, such as along rivers, creeks and streams.

Look for natural riffles, both under water and below the high water mark. These may be Indian grinding rocks, pot holes, cracks, crevices, or any low spot that can slow down the water enough to let the GOLD settle to the bottom (bedrock). Natural GOLD settling spots are bends in a stream where sand and gravel bars form, also a sunken water-logged tree, a small rock barrier or dam that possibly children built for a swimming hole, even a beaver dam, in fact—anything that slows the water enough for GOLD to drop. Above the water level on dry land that has been flooded, there may be moss growing on rocks or at the base of trees. This, too, holds GOLD. (See "Mossing"). The top of a hill or mountain could be a Bench Placer of a tertiary river bed that has never been eroded or discovered. A canyon wall or ravine could have GOLD exposed by recent rains or a slide. Maybe no one ever looked there, or if they did, it may not have been exposed then. Remember, too, that every day of the year more sand and rocks and even GOLD are being washed down from hidden sources higher up in the mountains.

# Where To Look For Gold

GOLD has even been absorbed by plants and when these plants are dried and burned, the ashes are panned and GOLD is found in the ashes. Even small plants when pulled up have had GOLD sometimes clinging to their roots. If you know where a well is being dug, pan this dirt as it is removed. It may surprise you. Check new road construction cuts and slides, or anywhere new earth has been exposed. All are possibilities. Other places are new swimming pools, tank holes for a new gasoline station, even terracing a back yard. Explore the foundations of some old buildings being torn down.

Some parts of the State have never been fully explored for GOLD. Starting in Northern California, there are the Klamath Mountains and River area. This extends 130 miles along the northwest coast of California to the interior Cascade range. This also includes the Trinity, Salmon and Siskiyou Mountains. GOLD-bearing gravels have been found in many canyons. This is very rugged country and some of it is still quite primitive, like the Marble Mountain area. Around the areas of old Shasta City, Yreka and Redding is also GOLD country. See the $80,000 native GOLD display in the Yreka Courthouse foyer.

Reaching from Sierra County in the north to Mariposa County on the south, is a 120-mile stretch of the Sierra Nevada mountain range known as the "Mother Lode." It is in this section that the GOLD era played the major part in the history of California during the 1849 period. It is in this same area today that the pleasure seeking, GOLD hunting prospectors spend their weekends, enjoying the excitement of finding GOLD in the streams that wend their way down the western slopes. Every member of the family, both young and old, have fun searching for GOLD. Along the Mother Lode are many historic GOLD towns marking the area where GOLD was and is found. A random sampling of the names of some towns are: Downieville, Nevada City, Grass Valley, Auburn, Coloma, Placerville, Drytown, Sutter Creek, Jackson, San Andreas, Columbia, Sonora and Mariposa.

Whenever a dam is placed on a river, as the Folsom Dam is on the American River, there is little chance of finding much GOLD below the dam—that is, on the river bed itself. But, at higher elevations above the water, there may be GOLD that has not been moved or disturbed. The area above a dam can still contain GOLD. In fact, when the Hell Hole Dam broke in January 1965 releasing its tremendous surge of water down the Rubicon River into the Middle Fork of the American River, it took everything with it,

# Where To Look For Gold.

sweeping away trees, boulders—even bridges. It created slides, tore out old river bars and channels, and relocated everything for miles. It exposed bedrock never before seen by man. This event is enticing the amateur prospector and GOLD miner with pans, gasoline-powered sluice boxes, even rockers and suction dredges. Lots of color has been appearing, and quite a few good-sized nuggets. In fact, this area has brought out one of the largest collections of amateur prospectors in years.

Now we approach the southeastern section of California. Here are vast waste lands and desert where GOLD mining in the alluvial fans and flat lands has brought new adventure to the desert prospectors. They are using dry mining methods such as winnowing, hand and gasoline operated vibrators and shakers, as well as dry washers. Wherever there is water, panning and some rocker mining exists. Anyone going into the desert or waste lands must be careful not to get lost or stranded. The desert heat affects some, too. It is not too populated in case help is needed. Water is a very important item on any list. An article in the *Desert Magazine* dated June 1949 is interesting. "There's Placer Gold in Desert Bajadas." Check your library for a copy.

Our next area where some GOLD has been found is the ocean beaches. During the '30s the beaches were panned and sluiced in the Santa Cruz area, especially around Capitola. The ocean waters contain much GOLD, but one has yet to find a cheap method of recovery. Ideas for this are still open and welcome.

The main thing that I am trying to point out is that GOLD may be found almost anywhere. Many times it is where one least expects it to be. That is why a little study of what happened to the earth thousands of years ago will help you to see how the land has moved, taking whatever it had with it to another place. Remember once again GOLD seeks the lowest places. Wherever it is stopped, there it waits for you.

If you want to try prospecting or panning on private property, be sure to ask permission of the owners. They may let you work some old tailings of a mine, or even dig a little. Remember that this is private property, and when someone permits you to prospect, protect their property. Do not leave litter and create any problem so that the owners will not let anyone try again. There are commercial GOLD panning places around the State where for a small fee you learn to pan their ore and keep the GOLD you find. Besides, they give you professional help.

# What Is Placer Mining?

It is the process of removing GOLD from placer deposits. Placer mining is easier and cheaper to do than hard rock mining. Be sure to ask permission of the owners. They may let you work veins or lodes. The easiest placers to work are the surface deposits, usually along a quiet stream or nearby banks and hills. Remember placer GOLD is always found near bedrock. The equipment used in placer mining varies with the type of deposit, soil and miner. While the GOLD pan is traditional, other equipment is: rockers, sluice box, long tom, mud box, dredge and others.

# What Are Placers?

There are two basic types. First, *residual placers* are where the GOLD and gravels are in their original lodes, but the auriferous rocks are decomposed. Second, the *transported placers* are the residual placers that have been moved and scattered across the lands below. They may be moved by floods, rivers, creeks or land movements such as slides, earthquakes or construction projects.

Examples of transported placers:

(1) Creek Placers—where gravel deposits are in creek and river beds spread across flooded plains and general low lands, and left near the surface.

(2) Bench placers are the remnants of ancient tertiary stream channels, followed by cross channels cut in the quatenary period, which left gravel deposits in layers or spread out from 50 to several hundred feet above the present streams.

(3) Hillside placers are deposits of gravel found between creek and bench placers.

(4) River Bar placers are found in flat gravel beds in or adjacent to the beds of large streams. This may be large sand or gravel bars located on the slow moving side of a stream, while the deeper and faster moving water channel goes around the far side of them.

(5) Gravel-Plain placers are in gravels in both the coastal areas and the lowland plains.

(6) Sea-Beach placers are relocated placers by the ocean wave action along the sea shore, either in gravel or sand beaches.

(7) Ancient Beach placers may be found inland, deposited by early inland seas, or along the coastal plains along the lines of elevated benches.

(8) Lake Bed placers are widespread areas caused by lakes being formed from glacial drainage, land slides, mountain movements leaving concentrated and accumulated GOLD-bearing deposits and gravel trapped.

# Gold Panning

GOLD PANNING
"Shake gold pan to settle gold into lower bend of the pan"

GOLD PANNING
"Dip to float out lighter materials three times, then shake
to resettle"

# Gold Panning

Panning for GOLD has continued down through the years, both as a hobby and for the more serious minded. For with the panning method GOLD is still found every day, not only in the streams, but on the hillsides too. With a traditional GOLD pan and a little water you can sample the auriferous gravels at any of the spots mentioned in "Where to Find GOLD."

The GOLD pan is usually made of heavy gauge steel shaped into a shallow pan which varies from 12 to 18 inches in diameter at the top, and from 2 to 2½ inches in depth, with the sides having a 30° slope. To stiffen the pan, the rim is turned back over a heavy wire. Pans weigh from 2 to 3 lbs.

In this chapter I am going to pass on some of the tricks of panning which I have learned from old-time panners, and 35 years of practical experience. First, never use grease or oil near GOLD. Watch the use of hand lotions, and if you have naturally oily skin you should scrub often. When you purchase a new steel GOLD pan it will have a greasy protection film. This should be removed by gasoline or *burning out*. Generally you should burn out the pan and scour with sand. Remember any grease, oil or fat will attach to GOLD and it will float out of your pan.

Before you actually start GOLD panning you should practice in your backyard, a stream, or commercial "Dude" mines. For backyard panning practice get a galvanized tub, which is always helpful in GOLD mining. Fill the tub 2/3 or 3/4 full of water. Now you will need some heavy material to substitute for GOLD. Lead or buckshot have been used. Buckshot is best because of its size, and if flattened it is better. Place the buckshot in a half pan of dirt. Now you are ready to pan. Just pretend the metal is GOLD. Here is how.

With a little over half a pan of gravel, GOLD (buckshot), and enough water to cover the dirt, hold the pan with one hand on each side about the center, dividing the weight equally. Use somewhat sudden or quick jerks that make the material in the pan separate, this also starts the heavy metals to settle on the bottom. Of course these movements must not let either water or material leave the pan. After possibly a dozen of these movements, tip the pan slightly away from you and dip about a fourth of the pan in the water to let

# Gold Panning

some of the loose dirt and mud float out of the pan. Dip and pour slowly most of the surplus water off. Dip again and get clean water in the pan. Now, use a rotating, oscillating motion in somewhat of an oval pattern to set the water and material in the pan to moving about, thus creating a better separation of light and heavy material. Then dip gain and remove more of the dirty water. Repeat this process of separating and floating off the dirty water until you have fairly clean sand and small gravel. Any large rocks should be washed off and inspected then thrown away if they contain no GOLD. Hand pick all the gravel and inspect also.

When just sand is left, pan some more with the same movements. This time you will begin to remove, by floating out, the grey sand. Here it is very necessary not to float out the finer GOLD, and you must keep the heavy material settled continuously on the bottom. Dip and let the grey sand slip off the edge of the pan a couple of dips. Resettle and dip again. Do this until just the black sand is left. To inspect your find, you now dip about half a cup of water in the pan. With rotating slow movement you make the water slowly roll around the inside edge of the pan in a counter clockwise motion. This will move the black sand in a circular movement away from the main pile. As this is done, watch the edge where the sand is moving away from for colors. That is fine GOLD. As the sand is slowly moved away, the heavy GOLD will be seen (or your buckshot). Now at this point, any flakes that show up can be removed with either tweezers or a wet wooden match stick or twig and put in your small glass vial. When you are satisfied that you have all the larger pieces, pour the sand into a wide-mouth jar. Wash from the pan so you will not lose any of the sand or flour GOLD. When practicing with buckshot, put in ten pieces and get ten back. It is a cheap substitute for GOLD.

Later recover the balance of GOLD from your jar of sand by the recovery vibrator.

# Mossing

"Mossing" is a simple placer mining method. It is the gathering of moss from rock ledges as well as from the base of trees in a flood or overflow area. Moss acts like a natural sponge and collects GOLD from flour to fair-size grains and tends to hold it tightly.

Mossing should be done slow and easy, as rough handling or sudden violent movements will dislodge the GOLD. Remember, too, that much of the GOLD that is collected in the moss slowly settles to the bottom. So wherever moss is growing, more GOLD may be found either at the base or even below. Clean thoroughly all that area where the GOLD may be. Dig or scrape around rocks and tree stumps under the moss and place the material into your GOLD pan.

Fill your pan about one-third full of water and set on level ground. With your hands, pull apart the moss in the water and separate. After the moss has been shredded and washed out clean in your GOLD pan, put the moss in a box or on a cloth to dry. This will take a few days. Burn the dried moss in a metal container and pan the ashes for any GOLD that is left.

After cleaning the moss, then work the cracks under the moss. This is known as "crevicing."

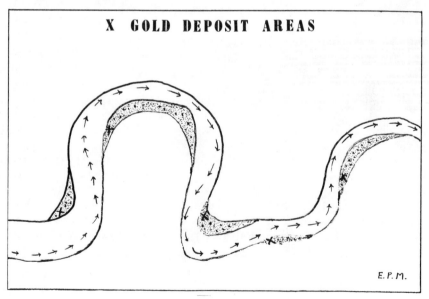

X GOLD DEPOSIT AREAS

E. P. M.

**Author's Drawing**

RIVER AND GRAVEL BARS
"X's mark where GOLD settles as water slows down."

# Crevicing

After winter floods have eroded mountain tops and uncovered minerals and rocks long buried, the spring run off carries them tumbling down. GOLD, being heavy, will settle in crevices, cracks, depressions, potholes and natural riffles.

When you discover a likely spot, any of the following tools may prove useful, depending on the depth, size, hardness and accessibility of the rocky bottom. A good stiff wire or crevicing tool, screwdriver or tweezers, whisk broom and pan may be the only equipment you can use. However, to really clean out and collect all the deep deposited GOLD you may need a pick and shovel, crow bar, even drifts, wedges and gouges, sledge hammers and scrapers.

Sweep carefully all fine sand from any ledges into a dust pan or GOLD pan. Then use a crevicing tool or stiff wire hook to clean out the cracks right to, and especially the very bottom. It is possible here to see GOLD coming into your pan. Leave no crack uncleaned. It is sometimes necessary to put a bar into the crack and break off the outside slab and clean deeper to the bottom of the rock. Often at the bottom of some cracks solid packed layers of fine GOLD are found—even nuggets. This is treasure hunting, and one never knows what waits for him. Some prospectors have used jacks to pry larger slabs apart in order to get to the very bottom. For the larger depressions and potholes and Indian grinding rocks, use a tin cup or can to scrape the bottom clean. Pour in water and sniff up the remainder.

One of the most useful tools for cracks under water is the GOLD sniffer. A syringe type sniffer could be made from a large clean grease gun—preferably new, as it must contain absolutely no grease. The best type has the front or nozzle end that unscrews. This is better for cleaning and unloading. Of course, you may make a GOLD sniffer (instructions in book) from many different items and materials. The purpose is to have enough suction to pull up GOLD.

# Crevicing

Use a drawback syringe type, with a small enough nozzle to reach into the small cracks. Water is necessary if you are to get the best results. Place the nozzle to the bottom of the crack and draw back on the plunger, keeping the nozzle very close to the bottom. With the plunger still back, turn nozzle up and unscrew top tip and pour contents into pan or bucket. Screw on top and repeat. This is sniffing for GOLD. The old stand-by GOLD pan is needed to complete the recovery.

A lucky crevicer could find more GOLD than just panning, rocking, or sluicing, depending, of course, on the place, soil and conditions. The accumulated GOLD found in these depressions goes on year after year, and even though you cleaned it last year, more may be returning to it today. Whenever you find a good rich crack or crevice, make a note of the exact location in your book of "GOLDEN Notes." Thus every year you can return and harvest a new crop. Sometimes man makes GOLD drop where nature can help him recover it more easily.

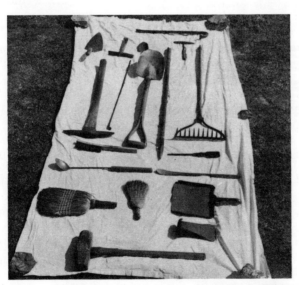

Author's Photo

CREVICING TOOLS
"Some of the many useful crevicing tools."

# The Gold Rocker

The rocker, designed similar to a child's cradle was one of the first pieces of machinery to be used in placer mining. It made its first California appearance March 9, 1848, at Coloma—GOLD discovery site. Within a very short time many rockers were being built and used, because they were faster than the GOLD pan or batea. In the rocker you can recover all heavy materials such as tin, tungsten, ore, cinnabar, platinum metals, and even gem stones, while the lighter materials will float off as tailings. Both the apron and riffles gives you greater concentrating and collecting areas than the GOLD pan.

### Rocker Body

Rockers were built in various shapes and sizes. The floor is mounted on traverse rockers. The sides and one end form a tight enclosure with the other end open for run-off. The sides may be straight or sloped outward on top from 1 to 3 inches. The height of the sides depends on the size of apron and hopper box built. The hopper box is mounted on the enclosed end, called the head of the rocker.

### Hopper Box or Grizzly

The hopper box may be permanent or removable; the metal grading plate, however, should be removable. The shape of a hopper box is either square or rectangular. A handle may be attached to the hopper or to the rocker body. The depth of the hopper is between 3 and 8 inches. The hopper box with the grading screen as its floor is mounted on the top of the rocker at the head, with the apron beneath.

### Grading Plate or Screen

This iron or steel plate is from 1/8 to 1/4 inch thick. Evenly spaced holes of 3/8 to 1/2 inch diameter, with about the same space between holes, cover the plate surface. This plate should be removable.

# The Gold Rocker

### Apron

The apron is made of canvas or blanketing stretched loosely over a wooden removable frame. It is set directly beneath the grading plate to catch the material which comes through the screen in a loose sagging section while the lighter weight material falls off and flows forward to the riffles.

### Carpet or Blanket

A section of carpeting or blanket cut the same size as the riffle is placed flat on the floor of the rocker. This holds the fine GOLD and black sand. It is held in place with wire mesh (riffle screen) and the riffles.

### Riffle Screen

This is an addition to help recover more GOLD than just the permanent riffles. Use a lath screen or expanded metal with the angle portions facing into the flow of water from the head of the rocker. The screen is held in place by the riffles on top pushing down by the force of the wedges driven from above. The purpose is to give an added boiling effect and push the GOLD and heavy materials down into the carpet or blanketing below, while the lighter materials float up and away. The screen is cut the same size as the blanket and riffles.

### Riffles

Riffles are the obstructions that slow down the movement of heavy materials so they will fall and become trapped. They are usually made of wood with a slight angle at the bottom. These hold down the riffle screen and the carpeting.

### Wedges

In a rocker with removable riffles, four wedges are usually used to force down the riffles, riffle screen and carpeting. Enough pressure is necessary to make these as water tight as possible. If any water leaks out, it may take fine GOLD with it.

# Rocker Operation

Now for a complete run-down on the operation of the rocker. First, locate your site and make a sampling with a GOLD pan to see if and how much "color" is there. If sample proves good, set up your rocker near running or a *bucket water* supply. Check the type and size of material to be worked, and determine the slope of the rocker needed. Too much slope will cause some GOLD to float out. At no time would more than 3" ever be necessary. The average placer will work at a 1" or 2" raise. Use either boards or flat rocks to elevate the head of the rocker. Use a shovel to place material into the hopper box. Do not overload, as you can always add more.

Now, over this material slowly pour water with a dipper, and gently rock the rocker. Continue adding water and rocking until the loose material has fallen through the grading screen. At this point, inspect the rocks for nuggets or GOLD embedded in quartz. The nuggets you save, of course, and quartz with GOLD embedded must be crushed (See "Crushing") or saved as specimens. The remaining rocks are thrown away, and you load up again and repeat the process.

If there is lots of clay, this must be broken down into a flowing muddy water in order to remove the GOLD. Any clay lumps can and will rob the GOLD from the riffles and carry it out of the rocker. Be sure to wash all roots, moss and grass in hopper. It is best that you learn to identify the different rocks, minerals and metals. This way you are less apt to discard something valuable besides GOLD.

# Cleanup

Stop adding materials to rocker's hopper box. Continue washing the materials and remove all rocks and gravel from grading plate. Lift up plate and wash all sides over apron. Then set aside the plate. Next remove all visible GOLD from the apron pocket and place in your jar. Carefully remove the apron and place in a tub or over your GOLD pan and wash clean. Also set this aside. Inspect the rocker floor for visible GOLD. Remove to your jar then wash the inside walls and floor so that everything washes toward the riffles. Place a pan or tub under the tailing end of the rocker. Remove all wedges and wash off. Next carefully remove the

# Cleanup

riffles, place in tub and wash all sides. Do the same with the riffle screen. With much care, slide the carpeting off the end and directly into the tub with no loss of material. Pour water slowly into the rocker and wash all remaining sand and GOLD into the pan or tub. Rub and scrub carpeting well in water in the tub to remove all sand and fine GOLD. When the carpeting begins to show wear, burn in a metal container and pan the ashes to recover hidden GOLD.

# Back In Operation

To reassemble, first lay in the carpeting followed by the metal screen, then place the riffles on top of that and tap in the wedges. Replace the apron and the grading plate. If you have a partner, he can start mining while you work down the concentrate. Otherwise, pour off the excess water in the tub and try your hand at another batch. Later on at home you can clean up the tub full of good materials in evening spare time.

Courtesy of Ott Heizer
California Division of Mines and Geology
CHINESE MINER
"Chinese with portable rocker".

# Rocker In Action

### ROCKER IN ACTION
"Material - Water - Rocking Gets GOLD."

### ROCKER CLEAN UP
"Wash parts clean and assemble rocker."

# Sluice Box

The sluice box is another method of working auriferous sands and gravels to extract the GOLD contained therein. Sluicing has been done since the 1849 period when it was considered a good fast way to get GOLD. It was later improved by the "Long Tom." Sluicing as a method was occasionally done in a ditch instead of in a box. The box, though, is somewhat handier and easier to control, for within the box you can place riffles to collect the GOLD and it is easier to clean up without extra loss.

Though the sluice is a crude type of box, it still serves the purpose. A good set of riffles in either one long box, or one box of riffles and another for sluicing is used. The dimensions depend upon how many will be working the box, the amount of material you want to push through the box, and the type of material you will sluice. The slope on a sluice ranges from 5 to 18 inches for every 12 feet of sluice. Different types of riffles may be used as well as the number you require. In the sluice there usually is no receiving box, although a grizzly may be built.

Normally the material is shoveled directly into the grizzly box or upper sluice while the water is flowing by. Here the large rocks and very coarse materials are removed by hand. The material that remains helps to polish the rusty and dirty GOLD making it easier to see and it will amalgamate easier if you use quicksilver. When operating properly, the water should carry away all the tailings, and in the sluice wash the material clean and separate it. The regulation of the water that enters the header box is very important as too much will wash out much of the GOLD, while too little allows the riffles to clog and the tailings to stack up. A person can work with a sluice from six feet long in a single length to a couple of hundred feet long, by proper control of the water and the amount of material shoveled into the sluice. Of course a sluice box takes lots more water than a rocker or pan, and this must be considered.

A settling dam or hole at the tailing end of a long tom, sluice or rocker should be made to prevent muddy water and silt from entering a stream. This protects fish feeding and spawning by letting the mud settle.

# Sluice Box

### SLUICE BOX
"Sluice Box is faster than rocker or pan."

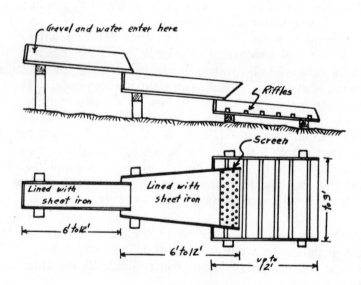

### LONG TOM
Courtesy of California Division of Mines and Geology

# Long Tom

The "Long Tom" is one of the more popular pieces of equipment for one or more men to operate. It is an inclined trough or box similar to a sluice (water tight, of course, as a sluice must be) and preferably built of smooth lumber (same for the sluice). It is usually built in two sections—a sluice box and a riffle section. A grizzly may be added. Use a slope of about one inch per foot.

The sluice section is usually about 12 feet long. The header, or upper end, is from 15 to 24 inches wide, while the lower end may be from 24 to 36 inches wide. The sides are from 8 to 10 inches high. The sluice portion is above the riffle section and contains a metal screen or perforated plate to keep the coarse materials out of the riffles.

The riffle section is usually shorter than the sluice part, as well as being wider - about two inches wider than the end of the sluice - and four to six feet long. Removable riffles are helpful in the clean-up. Added screen and carpeting will help to hold more GOLD.

A Long Tom is operated in the same manner as a sluice, except that more men operate for faster recovery. Shovel the material into a grizzly (if used) or into the sluice section, and let the water pour over the material, washing it farther down the sluice. The large rocks are picked out and inspected by hand, while the coarser materials are kept out of the riffles with the screen or perforated plate.

Clean up is done as often as seems necessary. Stop the flow of water after the sluice section has been cleaned. Clean up the catch screen. Remove the wedges that hold down the riffles. Clean the riffles exactly as described for the rocker and sluice box. Remove them in order and wash each part into the tub—riffles, then screen, followed by the carpeting. Scrub the carpeting into the tub. Replace the parts and resume operation.

Check the grading screen or perforated plate often as this sometimes catches GOLD.

# Mud Box

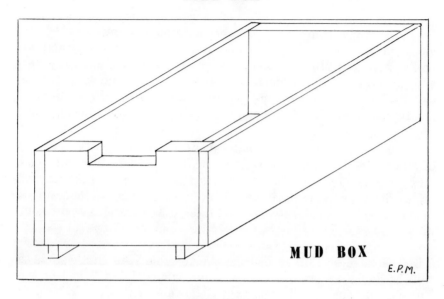

**MUD BOX**

**MUD BOX**
"Use on top of sluice box to separate clay from GOLD."

Author's Photo

**PUDDLING BOX**
"Puddling box for clayey materials at the head of a sluice box."

# Mud Box

The mud box was first used at Michigan Bar, where most of the GOLD-bearing soil was clay. It was a box any size one wished to make it. A fairly standard size seemed to be 15 inches wide and 30 inches long and 10 inches deep. One end had a notch cut in it about 2 inches deep and about 8 inches wide. Through this lower section the overflow water went down into the sluice box. The mud box was made water tight and placed across the head end of a long sluice and held in place with two cleats.

Clay material was placed in this box with a given amount of water allowed to flow continuously into it. This mixed the clay into a muddy watered solution that would flow down through the sluice and the riffles. Any gravel encountered was washed, inspected and discarded. Usually little gravel is found in clay pits. With constant mixing, the dissolved watery clay would flow through the riffles and the heavy GOLD stayed there. Of course, even this method did not save all the GOLD as much floated away.

When clean up time came, the mud box was worked until clean. When clear water flowed out, the box was inspected, then what was left was panned. Sometimes large amounts of GOLD were found, as the box acted as a catch basin.

# Puddling Box

Another similar type was the puddling box. This was just an open, straight sluice at the head of the main long sluice box where clay was broken down and flowed on through and over the riffles. The clayey material was shoveled into this box and broken up with a hoe or rake before it passed into the main sluice, as unbroken lumps of clay in a sluice may pick up and carry away the GOLD particles.

# Powered Dry Washer

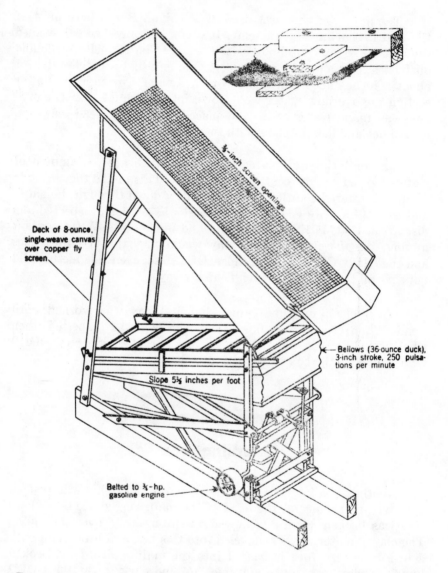

Power-driven dry washer, capacity 0.8 cubic yards per hour. Goler Gulch, California, (June 1932)

## DRY PLACER BELLOWS

Courtesy of California Division of Mines and Geology
"Use where water is scarce or not available. Hand or gas-powered."

# Dry Placer

Dry placer deposits have been mined in a number of areas in the desert regions of southeastern California where very little water is available. In these arid regions, the GOLD cannot be recovered by conventional wet methods, hence dry methods employing air have been devised. Dry concentration is much slower and less efficient than wet concentration and can only be used on dry small-sized particles that can be moved by the force of air.

A popular dry washer of the bellows type is shown in the accompanying figure. Here the coarse particles must be separated out. This is accomplished by shoveling the gravel to be concentrated onto the screen where the coarse materials pass off the lower end and the fines go into the hopper. From the low end of the hopper, the sand falls onto the riffles. Air from the bellows lifts the lighter particles of sand over the riffles and off the low end of the washer, while the heavier particles of GOLD and black sand remain back of the riffles. The machine is operated either by a gasoline engine or by hand crank. The crankshaft is equipped with a cam to vibrate the screen. The shaft transmits power to an eccentric which operates the bellows.

To insure a flat surface and an even distribution of air in the GOLD recovery section, a riffle unit is built up as follows: a well braced piece of window or fly screen is covered with a handkerchief linen above which the riffles are placed, from 4 to 6 inches apart. The riffles are made of 1/2 to 3/4 inch half-round moulding with the flat face on the upper side. If amalgamation of the flour GOLD is desired, pockets holding quicksilver are placed in front of the riffles. Some flour GOLD also passes through the handkerchief linen and is caught in the burlap.

A power washer of this type can handle up to 0.8 cubic yards per hour. Hand washers operated by two men have a capacity of 1 or more cubic yards per eight-hour shift, depending upon the size and nature of the gavel to be handled.

The most productive dry placer-mining GOLD districts have been in the El Paso Mountains and at Randsburg, San Bernardino County, and the Cargo Muchacho Mountains, Chocolate Mountains, Picacho, and Potholes areas in Imperial County. Much of the GOLD produced in these districts by dry concentration methods years ago was done by Mexicans and Indians in small one- or two-man operations using hand-operated dry washers.

# Winnowing

Ideal ground for dry concentration is difficult to find. Once the dry surface is penetrated, most ground will be found to contain sufficient moisture to prevent separation of the light and heavy particles. The moisture content of "dry placers" thus is the principal obstacle to dry concentration.

Winnowing is the fundamental dry method. This is accomplished by first screening out the coarse gravels using a screening box or grizzly. This is a strong wooden frame with a screen bottom. The frame is placed in the center of a blanket or canvas. Skim off the top soil with a shovel and place it in the screening box. Lift the box and sift the lighter materials onto the blanket. Inspect the remaining material in the box for GOLD then pile it nearby. Two people, each holding two corners of the blanket, toss the contents into the air. The lighter particles blow or drift away, letting the heavier materials fall back onto the blanket. It sometimes has been necessary to crush or pulverize the earth before winnowing.

Later, when the blanket shows signs of wear, scrub or burn, then pan the ashes to recover the GOLD that the weave of the blanket tends to hold.

Courtesy of California Division of Mines and Geology
"Winnowing dry placers by air."

WINNOWING

Winnowing GOLD near Chinese Camp, from "California," a book for travelers and settlers, by Charles Nordhoff, 1873.

# Ore Crushing

### SINGLE MILL
"Use a young tree for single stamp mill."

### GANG MILL
"Gang type stamp mill. Multi stamp mills' power:
Animal - water - gas - steam."

### ARRASTRA
"Cheapest method for crushing ore. Build an arrastra."

# Ore Crushing

To the amateur prospector ore crushing seldom is necessary, yet it is possible that somewhere along the way you may have need of small-scale crushing. Once in a while you find a place where there is a small outcropping of quartz that contains GOLD—even leaf GOLD. The size and amount of material to be crushed determines the size and type of crusher you will need. It may be necessary to roughly break down some material with a sledge hammer to a size you can use in your crusher. Of course, if this is necessary, be careful not to lose the GOLD in the primary breaking stage.

### Mortar and Pestle

Small crushers as the iron or steel mortar and pestle can be made. See instructions in this book. The idea is the same for most sizes you may want. Place your material in the mortar and put the pestle part on top. Strike with large hammer. Continue driving down the hammer, rotating large rock lumps once in a while in the mortar. When crushed to powder, pan out the flour GOLD.

### Stamp Mill

A simple stamp mill can be made with the help of a bent-over sappling with a weight or plunger tied to the tip end. The operator raises the weight with the aid of the sappling's spring and pounds into a rock basin or iron kettle or rock-layed base such as an arrastra. I once saw a small four-stamp mill made of a worn out auto motor block, using special made pistons and a special compartment where the oil pan should be to hold the GOLD being crushed. A little imagination and ingenuity can go a long way. Necessity becomes the mother of inventions.

# Ore Crushing

## Arrastra

You may build an arrastra if you need more ore crushed. This is a circular basin lined with rock—both the floor and side walls—with a center post from which your drag will ride. If a mixture of sloppy clay is poured into the space around the rocks on the floor and part way up the wall, then smoothed to level with the face of the rocks, a fire may be built to bake the clay inside the arrastra. Horse power (or mule) was mostly used, but other means can be employed.

A cement mixer with either iron balls or very hard rocks can act as the grinding element, but you will need power—gasoline or electricity. If you are lucky, maybe you can harness water power. I helped cut a Model T Ford short in length to make what might be called a tractor. This was driven around an arrastra pulling the sweeps to which drag stones were attached. These ground the quartz ore to powder. We called it our mechanical mule.

The arrastra is a cheap and good ore grinder for both GOLD and silver ores. Sometimes called a drag mill, it was first introduced by the early Mexican miners. At one time California had thousands of them. Many can still be found today. In one district in Southern California, known now as Riverside County, once could be seen the ruins of no less than 125 arrastra basins built and operated by the Mexicans that hauled in the ore to what was known as Arrastra Canyon.

The arrastra is essentially a fine-grinding and amalgamating machine suitable for ores from 3/4 inch to 100 mesh. Although the arrastra has been largely superseded by stamp mills, ball mills, etc., it still remains one of the cheapest and best GOLD-saving devices where small rich veins are to be worked in more or less inaccessible and remote regions. Its chief advantages are that it can be built by a man of limited mechanical skill from materials to be had almost anywhere. These mills may range from 3 feet to 12 or more feet in diameter with crushing capacity of 3 to 6 tons daily. Any power may be used: horse, mule, water wheel, gas and steam engine, even electric power. But, remember, slow speed is necessary. Water-powered over-shot wheels are cheapest and give slow speed.

# Gold Recovery By Vibrator

Some amateur prospectors find it difficult to remove the GOLD from the black sand. Because of this, I want to pass on a method I have used for many years. (See Vibrator Construction). When you have built this vibrating table you can and will enjoy GOLD recovery with it.

First, *dry* your black sand either in a flat pan in the oven or by time and evaporation. Place your vibrator at a long angle, say three inches up. Turn on motor and place recovery pan at base. Slowly pour sand across the velvet at the top—not more than two tablespoons to begin. Watch how the sand slides down the velvet. If too slow, raise another inch. Repeat the positioning until the sand moves down across the velvet smoothly, leaving the GOLD behind. Operate at as steep an angle as will safely hold back the GOLD. Watch very carefully the fine GOLD dust. The black sand is collected at the base in the recovery pan.

Stop vibrating any time you want to and pick up the GOLD and put it in a vial or jar. Be sure no GOLD goes off into the recovery pan. If in doubt, use quicksilver throughout the sand to recover any GOLD. Any fine GOLD left on the velvet is removed by laying the frame flat and rolling quicksilver over the velvet to collect the GOLD.

I save all the black sand. Most of these black materials can be removed by magnets, but even then flour or dust GOLD can be lifted without seeing it.

"Black sands" is a term commonly applied to alluvial deposits containing appreciable quantities of heavy dark-colored iron-bearing minerals, and conditions that were favorable for their deposition would also have been favorable for depositing GOLD. In general, black sands consist of hard minerals ranging in specific gravity from 3 to 7. Early research and study of black sands of the placer areas of California showed that the following minerals occur most frequently: magnetite, GOLD, ilmenite, garnet, zircon, hematite, chromite, platinum, iridosmine, mercury, amalgam, olivine, iron silicates, pyrite, monazite, copper, cinnabar, cassiterite, and corundum.

# Gold Recovery By Vibrator

To date, GOLD and the platinum group metals have been the chief minerals recovered from the black sands of California. Much of the GOLD in former beach deposits is tarnished or "rusty," making it difficult to save in the sluice box and on amalgamation plates. The GOLD in black sand concentations is entirely amenable to cyanidation and chlorination. Satisfactory amalgamation of the "rusty" GOLD usually can be accomplished by grinding the material to scour and brighten it so that it will be taken up on contact with mercury.

## Magnets and Black Sand

Many people remove all or most black sand from their GOLD with a magnet. This works all right, but very often GOLD dust and fine particles are also lifted with the sand.

If you want to make a sand lifter, use an aluminum salt or pepper shaker, kitchen size, with a screw-on lid. Make a hole in the center of the top lid large enough for a 1/8 inch rod. Use a 1/8 inch rod of brass or welding rod and thread one end up about 1/2 inch. The rod should be about two inches longer than your shaker. In the top of the rod, form a loop large enough for your finger. Next you need an iron magnet, preferably round, and just large enough to fit loosely inside the aluminum shaker. Drill a hole in the center of the magnet and tap threads in the hole to match those on the bottom of the rod. Pass the rod through your aluminum shaker lid and screw the magnet on the bottom. Now put the shaker and lid together, and the magnet is in the bottom of your shaker.

When you place the shaker on black sand now, the magnet will attract the metallic black sand and hold it to the shaker bottom. Lift it and the sand comes away too. Lower it over a piece of paper and lift the rod upward by the loop, pulling the magnet away from the shaker bottom. The black sand falls free and you are ready to repeat the process. Check closely. If any GOLD has been carried in the black sand, roll some mercury around in the sand and it will catch up the GOLD.

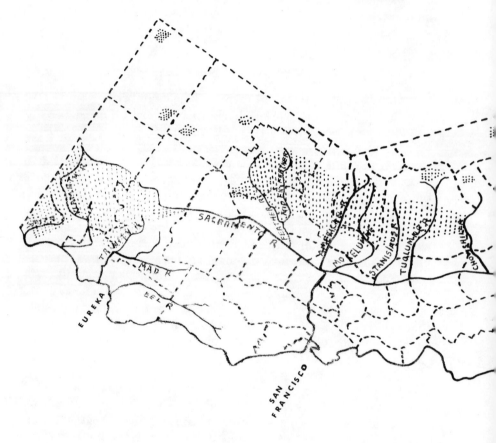

CALIFORNIA
GOLD-BEARING
AREAS
BORDERS
RIVERS

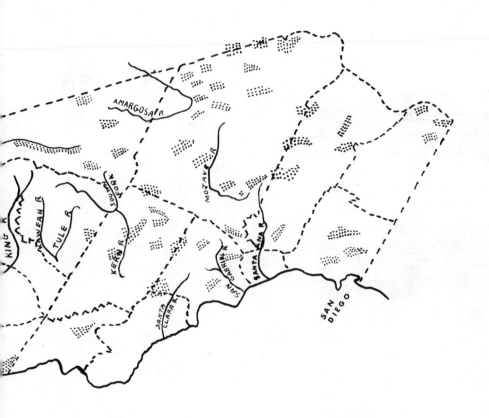

# Gold Amalgamation

This process is one of the oldest and simplest methods for recovering GOLD. When clean particles of GOLD are brought into contact with mercury, they form an alloy that is known as amalgam. The process is used to recover free GOLD in both lode and placer mining. In large-scale placer mining, the GOLD is amalgamated in sluices, riffle tables, or mechanical amalgamators. In small-scale placer mining, it is done in riffles or pans. In milling of lode GOLD ores, the finely ground ore is amalgamated on plates or it is jigged, and the jig concentrates are amalgamated. The GOLD is separated from the mercury by heating or by retorting, and the mercury may be recovered and used over again.

Mercury (or quicksilver) can be purchased from chemical supply houses and hardware or other stores that deal in miners' supplies. It usually comes in stoneware bottles or jugs, and it should be kept only in these or in iron or glass containers, because of its tendency to amalgamate with other metals. Only clean mercury should be used in amalgamating. Mercury is cleaned by retorting or straining through cloth or chamois skin.

### Pan Amalgamation

A small quantity of mercury is placed in an ordinary miner's pan with the concentrates and agitated under water until no more free GOLD can be observed. The waste sands are then panned off, care being taken not to lose any of the amalgam or fine drops of mercury which gradually run together into a single mass. During the amalgamation process, the GOLD gradually loses its color and becomes more brittle. The amalgam is a dull grayish-white pasty mass which varies in hardness and color according to the time of contact and size of the GOLD particles. Copper plated or copper bottomed pans are very useful for amalgamating. The copper should be cleaned thoroughly, and then mercury is rubbed into it until it has a bright shiny surface. Then the concentrates are added and agitated. As the amalgam forms it should be scraped off and more mercury added to keep the surface bright.

### Sluice Amalgamation

Mercury is carefully placed in the sluice boxes, where it finds its way into the riffles. All cracks and leaks in the sluice should be plugged. Some operators place mercury in the sluices before making a run, while others do it just before cleaning up. During the run, more mercury should be added periodically. There will always be some loss, especially where the grade is steep. The sluice box concentrates are then removed, washed, and the amalgam and mercury recovered by panning.

# Gold Amalgamation

### Plate Amalgamation

Amalgamating plates are used chiefly in lode GOLD milling, but occasionally they are used in placer mining. In this process, finely ground ore in the form of a thin pulp containing 25% or less solids passes over the plates which are set at a slight slope. The plates are composed of copper or silver-plated copper into which mercury has been worked to form a bright surface. As the amalgam accumulates, it is scraped off, and more mercury is added.

### Mechanical Amalgamators

There are a number of different types, but the most common are barrel amalgamators and pan amalgamators. These are used chiefly for cleaning up, but also they are useful for recovering fine GOLD from black sands. Amalgamating barrels are revolving steel or cast iron drums. The material to be treated is placed in the barrel with mercury, water, and a few iron or steel balls, and the barrel is turned slowly for an hour or two. It is then washed to remove the lighter material, and the amalgam and mercury are recovered by panning. Sometimes a weak solution of sodium cyanide is used to brighten the GOLD, but it should only be done by an experienced person because of the danger of poisoning. Occasionally quartz pebbles are used to clean the rusty GOLD. Pan amalgamators are flat-bottomed cylindrical tubs or barrels upon which metal shoes slide. The concentrate and mercury are placed in the pan with enough water to make the mass fluid, and the device is run one or two hours. Revolving cast iron bowls containing heavy balls occasionally are used. A small concrete mixer with round cobblestones is a convenient amalgamating device for the small- or medium-scale placer miner.

### Extracting GOLD from Amalgam

The GOLD-bearing amalgam should first be cleaned. This is done by washing and then straining out excess mercury through buckskin, chamois skin, or strong tight cloth such as canvas. All of this usually is done by hand and preferably under water. The clean amalgam is then heated or retorted to drive off the mercury, and GOLD sponge remains. Whenever amalgam is heated, great care should be made to avoid inhaling the mercury fumes as they are exceedingly poisonous.

If only a small amount is to be treated, the amalgam is heated on a flat iron surface such as a shovel until all of the mercury is driven off. A simple method for treating small amounts of amalgam and recovering the mercury is to heat the amalgam under half of

# Gold Amalgamation

a hollowed-out potato. The mercury condenses in the potato which later is crushed and panned for recovery of the mercury. Small amounts can also be retorted in a glass tube that is sealed and bent at one end. The amalgam is placed in the sealed end and heated, the mercury fumes condensing in the open end.

An old prospector once showed me how he retorted his quick-silver (mercury) without equipment, but he always lost most of the quicksilver. He would hollow out a potato, make three or four small sharp sticks like toothpicks, put the amalgam in the hollowed potato, place the toothpicks around the inside edge, then place on the other half potato and wrap in mud. This was placed in a fire built in a pit; then he said to get the heck out of there for a day, and especially not down wind, as the poisonous fumes that escape are dangerous. Of course, he also said, he sometimes lost some amalgam this way by exploding potatoes. Crush and pan the potato after removing the amalgam. This way you may recover some quicksilver inside the potato. Personally, I do not recommend anyone trying retorting. Just keep using the quicksilver until it's loaded, and when you have enough to be worthwhile, then let someone who does smelting do the job. It's safer.

Many times GOLD becomes coated with iron and sulphides. This is known as "rusty GOLD". No GOLD will amalgamate with quicksilver that is so coated. The best way to remove the coating is a tumbling action in a barrel or with coarse gravels through a sluice or rocker. This rubbing and chipping action wears away or chips off much of the coating. When the GOLD gets clean it can and will attach itself to quicksilver it contacts.

Usually 25 to 30 per cent of the GOLD is lost because of rust coatings. When one is not using quicksilver, he often tosses out the dark nuggets and grains as if they were a rusty nail, piece of iron, or another rock. So watch your sluice and rocker riffles for rusty discolored rocks, large and small. Some rust can be removed by acid to clean the GOLD, but learn first what you are doing or you may be in serious trouble. Grinding these rust-coated GOLD particles to powder makes it possible to recover larger percentages.

# Gold Amalgamation

## Retort

A typical retort that is used in many mining operations is a cast iron pot with a tight-fitting cover. The cover has a hole that is connected with the condenser pipe (see diagram). Capacities of these range from a few to several hundred pounds of amalgam. The condenser is an iron pipe 3 to 4 feet long which is encased in a larger pipe through which cooling water circulates. The inside of the pot is usually coated with a thin film of chalk, clay, or a mixture of clay and graphite to prevent GOLD from sticking to the iron, and it should be thoroughly dried before adding the charge. The retort is filled with amalgam to not over 2/3 of capacity. The cover is clamped on, and the retort is heated. A low heat is first applied and then increased just enough to allow the mercury to vaporize and condense. A steady trickle of mercury emerges from the pipe which discharges into a vessel. When no more mercury appears, the temperature is increased for a few minutes to drive the last of the mercury out of the retort. It then is allowed to cool.

The spongy mass of GOLD left after retorting can be sold to the U. S. Mint or a licensed GOLD buyer. No more than 200 ounces of retort sponge may be held by any person in the United States at any time.

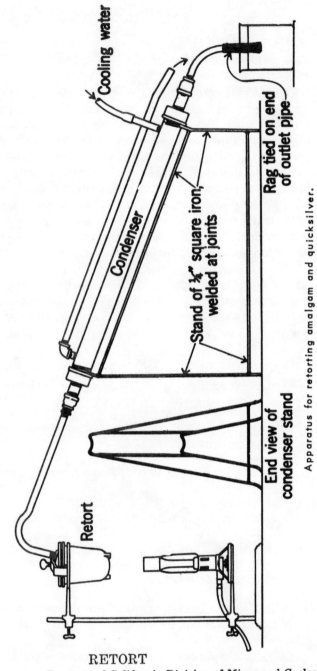

Cooling water

Condenser

Stand of ¼″ square iron, welded at joints

Rag tied on end of outlet pipe

End view of condenser stand

Apparatus for retorting amalgam and quicksilver.

Retort

RETORT

Courtesy of California Division of Mines and Geology

# Where To Sell Gold

Generally speaking, you may sell your GOLD to persons regularly engaged in the business of furnishing or processing GOLD for industry, profession, or art; or to the United States Mint. The first mentioned must be licensed buyers only.

It is unlawful for any person to engage in the business of milling, sampling, concentrating, reducing, refining, purchasing, or receiving for sale, ores, concentrates, or amalgams bearing GOLD or silver, GOLD dust, GOLD or silver bullion, nuggets, or specimens without first procuring a license as provided by the Public Resources Code, Division 2, Chapter 3 and amendments thereto. A license is not required for any mill, sampler, concentrating or reduction plant used exclusively by the owner in sampling, milling, or reducing or concentrating ores produced by such owner.

Two kinds of ore-buyers' licenses are issued: (1) *Limited,* limiting the buyers to $1,000 in purchases for the calendar year. (2) *Unlimited,* carrying no limit on purchases during the calendar year.

Persons with such a license keep and preserve a book in which they must enter:

(a) The name of the person on whose behalf such ores, concentrates, GOLD dust, GOLD or silver bullion, nuggets or specimens are delivered.

(b) The weight or amount and a short description of each lot.

(c) The name and location of the mine or claim from which it is stated that the lot has been mined or procured.

(d) The name of the person delivering it.

(e) The date of delivery.

(f) Whether the person making the delivery is a lessee, superintendent, foreman, or workman in such mine.

A monthly report of such purchases is made to the State Geologist.

# Diving For Gold

Skin diving for GOLD in California's rich streams has become increasingly popular since World War 2. Diving for GOLD is not new, but the equipment has been improved. GOLD diving in California was first attempted in 1849 on the American River near Sutter's Mill, Coloma. At that time the diving equipment was called "Subaqueous Armor." This venture was not successful. Because of the lack of knowledge and equipment during the 1850 to 1880's, mining on the rivers was accomplished by diversion of the water. The use of dams, tunnels, canals and flumes was employed to get to the river bottoms.

Around 1886-87 several crude suction dredges began operating along the rivers. They were equipped with steam-driven pumps with sluices. Divers were employed with these operations to remove obstacles and large rocks.

It was not until the end of World War 2 that diving for GOLD began to take shape. This was because of the discovery of self-contained underwater breathing apparatus known as SCUBA, which made it possible for almost anyone to be able to dive. Schools teaching skin diving soon became popular, as interest in this sport grew. They teach diving safety rules that prevent the "bends," getting trapped, and all other life saving rules. One of the best of these rules is the "Buddy System"—that is *Never dive alone.*

With the popularity of skin diving for GOLD, many new ideas and inventions began to appear—Rube GOLDbergs and all. Among these inventions came the well-known GOLD sniffer. Divers use the sniffer to remove GOLD from underwater crevics and natural riffles. (See "Crevicing"). Two divers are not only safer, but they can remove GOLD faster by changing operations. One may operate the sniffer while the other carries the bucket into which the GOLD is dumped.

## Snorkel Diving

For the shallow pools, the snorkel has proved helpful. This enables the diver to see and remove small quantities of sand and gravel which he pans out on shore at a later time.

## Suction Hose

In the beginning, a gasoline-powered pump was set up on the bank with a short sluice. The operator then waded out with a flexible hose and sucked the nearby sand and gravel to the sluice. Later, divers made board platforms, tied to truck-size inner tubes, which carried the gasoline motor and pump and the sluice box. This permitted the diver to work farther out and down to bedrock. The divers extended this method to get to the deeper holes. With this progress, another idea came about—the use of a dredge.

## Gold Dredge

The coming of the one-man to three-man dredges made it necessary to own a pick-up truck, trailer or station wagon. Also, more access roads to rivers and streams were needed. No longer could one pack into an area to mine with these large dredges which had single and double pontoons from 4 feet to 8 feet long. The operation became more than a hobby. There are many types of GOLD dredges on the market today. Some are better than others. Prices range from $100 to $1,000. Many places will sell you parts, which you assemble, while others will tailor-make any type you think you may need. It is wise to shop around before buying a dredge. Be sure you want and need one. Know where you can and will be able to use one.

A State permit is now required to operate a GOLD dredge. Check on county ordinances which may also apply. Do not gamble against laws of nature or man. The laws for the use of dredges began to be made to prevent stream pollution, destroying of fish food and spawning grounds. Also, do not trespass without written permission.

Large investments are necessary with the purchase of GOLD dredges, so before you go beyond the purchase of the old stand-by GOLD pan, know what you want to hunt for GOLD and how big an operation you want to engage in.

# The Legal Aspects

When you are just out for an interesting and enjoyable week end of GOLD panning, I have told you a good prospect is where GOLD has been found before—an old mine dump or tailings, or along favorable streams or rivers. The laws in general which affect you are: (1) Do not trespass on private property—always ask for permission. Information on land ownership can be obtained from plat maps in the offices of the County Assessor. Unfortunately, these maps do not distinguish between parts of the public lands open to prospecting and parts that already have been claimed, since surveys of claimed lands are not required until the property passes to patent or private ownership. The safest procedure, therefore, for the week end prospector and vacationist is to obtain permission from the residents on the property. (2) Do not cause fire. (3) Do no damage to river banks. (4) Cause no damage to fish. (5) Cause no pollution of the water.

I cannot cover all laws or regulations concerning placer mining in this book, because they are subject to change.

Conservation of fish and wildlife is a responsibility of the State and there are regulations concerning any activity *substantially* changing the bed channel, or bank of any river, stream or lake.

Section 5650 of the Fish and Game Code prohibits deposition in the State waters of any substance or material deleterious to fish.

Fish and Game Code, Sec. 5653, "Before any person uses any vacuum or suction dredge equipment in any river, stream or lake of this State, he shall submit an application to the Dept. of Fish and Game specifying the type and size of equipment to be used and the location where such equipment will be used"...

See Article 3 of the Fish and Game Code concerning regulations against mining operations in the Trinity and Klamath River Fish and Game District.

Any time you use a gasoline engine for any purpose, the State Division of Forestry requires you use a regulation spark arrestor to prevent fires.

Comply with safety regulations enforced by the State Division of Industrial Safety concerning abandoned excavations and transportation of explosives.

# The Legal Aspects

The California Division of Mines has many publications useful to the placer miner, both free and for sale. "Legal Guide for Prospectors and Miners," reprinted in 1965, covers "salient features needed by the average prospector and claim owner in initiating and maintaining his possessory rights to mineral ground." It is well worth the $1.00.

Once you locate a bonanza while prospecting for fun—

(1) Make sure it is on lands subject to location and purchase such as vacant public land, lands in National Forests or wherever mineral rights can be acquired.

(2) Stake your claim (mark the boundaries).

(3) Post a notice of the location on the spot. It should contain the date, name of discoverers, and the best legal description you can furnish, relating the location to some well-known landmark.

(4) Comply with State laws regarding recording the location in the county recorder's office, discovery work, etc.

(5) If you are not already in possession of the "Legal Guide for Prospectors and Miners" mentioned above, run—don't walk— to the nearest library and borrow a publication of the U. S. Dept. of the Interior, General Land Office, "Lode and Placer Mining Regulations" which explains how to file mineral claims, necessary annual assessment work, procedure to obtain patent, etc. Better yet, write for your own copy from the Government Printing Office.

(6) Within 90 days after the date of location a certain amount of Discovery work must be performed.

Always remember to keep California green and GOLDEN. Don't gamble with laws of man or nature.

# The Legal Aspects

## Federal GOLD Regulations

Under provisions of the Gold Reserve Act of 1934, the Director of the Mint may issue authorization permitting the acquisition and holding, transportation, melting and treating, importing and exporting of GOLD which the Director is satisfied is required for legitimate and customary use in industry, profession, or art, by persons regularly engaged in the business of furnishing or processing GOLD for industry, profession, or art, or for sale to the United States, or in an industry, profession, or art in which stocks of GOLD in excess of 50 fine troy ounces are required to be maintained by the applicant.

GOLD in its natural state means GOLD recovered from natural sources and which has not been melted, smelted, or refined, or otherwise treated by heating or by a chemical or electrical process; such GOLD may be acquired, transported within the United States, imported, or held in custody for domestic account without the necessity of holding a license therefor.

GOLD amalgam which results from the addition of mercury to GOLD in its natural state, recovered from natural deposits in the United States or a place subject to the jurisdiction thereof, may be heated to a temperature sufficient to separate the mercury from the GOLD (but not to the melting temperature of the GOLD) without a license by the person who recovered the GOLD from such deposits, or his duly authorized agent or employee. The retort sponge so resulting may be held and transported by such person without a license; provided, however, that no such person may hold at any one time an amount of such retort sponge which exceeds 200 troy ounces in fine GOLD content. Such retort sponge may be acquired from such persons by the United States or by persons holding licenses on forms obtained from the Director of the Mint, Treasury Department, Washington, D. C.

Except as provided in the Gold Reserve Act in secs. 54.12 to 54.20 inclusive, and in secs. 54.32 and 54.33, GOLD in its natural state may be melted or treated or exported only to the extent permitted by, and subject to the conditions prescribed in, or pursuant to secs. 54.21 to 54.27, inclusive.

Further information about and copies of Federal GOLD regulations may be obtained from the United States Mint.

# Construction of A Portable Rocker

A. End, one piece 1 in. x 14 in. x 16 in.

B. Sides, two pieces 1 in. x 14 in. x 48 in.

C. Bottom, one piece, 1 in. x 14 in. x 44 in.

D. Middle spreader, one piece 1 in. x 6 in. x 16 in.

E. End spreader, one piece 1 in. x 4 in. x 15 in.

F. Rockers, two pieces 2 in. x 6 in. x 17 in. (shaped).

H. Screen box about 16 in. square, outside dimensions, with screen bottom. Four pieces of 1 in. x 4 in. x 15-1/4 in. and one piece of screen 16 in. square with 1/4 in. or 1/2 in. openings or sheet metal perforated by similar openings.

K. Apron, made of 1 in. x 2 in. strips covered loosely with canvas. For cleats and apron, etc. 27 feet of 1 in. x 2 in. lumber is needed. Six pieces of 3/8 in. iron rod 19 in. long threaded 2 in. on each end and fitted with nuts and washers.

L. Handle, placed on the screen or on the body. When on the screen, it helps in lifting the screen from the body.

The parts are cut to size as shown on the drawing. The cleats on parts A, B, C, and D are of 1 x 2" material and are fastened with nails or screws. The screen box (H) is nailed together and the handle (L) is bolted to one side. Corners of the screen box should be reinforced with pieces of sheet metal because the screen is being continually pounded by rocks when the rocker is in use. The apron (K) is a frame nailed together, and canvas is fastened to the bottom. Joints at the corners should be strengthened with strips of tin or other metal. Through the center of each of the rockers a spike is placed to prevent slipping during operation. Two planks about 2 in. x 8 in. x 24 in. with a hole in center to hold the spike in the rockers are used as a bed for the rockers to work on and to adjust the slope of the bed of the rocker.

If one-quarter-inch lag screws are driven into the bottom of each rocker about 5 inches from each side of the spike and the heads are allowed to protrude from the wood, a slight bump will result as the machine is worked back and forth. This additional vibration will help to concentrate the GOLD. If screws are used, metal strips should be fastened to the bed-plates to protect the wood.

The construction of riffles is advisable and they should be made in such a way that they may be easily removed for clean up. Ten one-inch riffles spaced an inch apart would be about the right amount. Follow instructions for riffles given for a sluice box, but keep in proportion with rockers width.

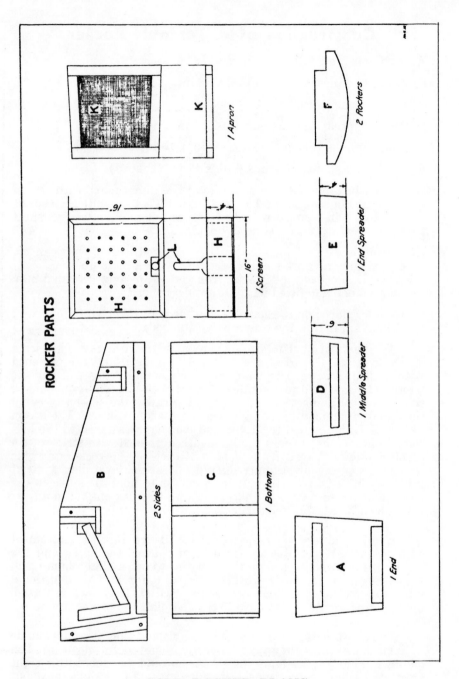

# GOLD ROCKER PLANS

Courtesy of California Division of Mines and Geology

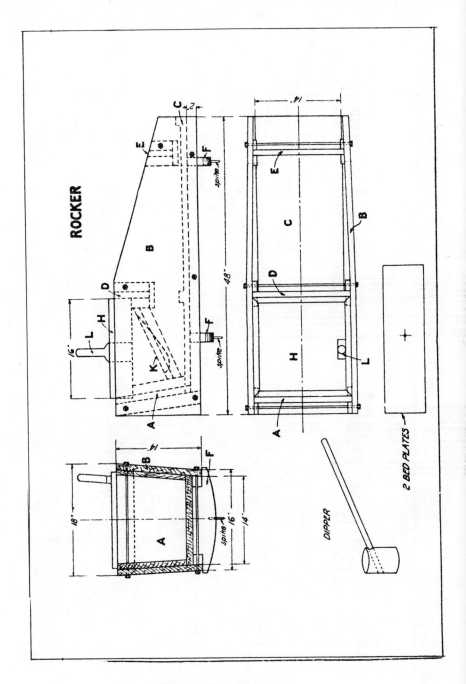

GOLD ROCKER PLANS

Courtesy of California Division of Mines and Geology

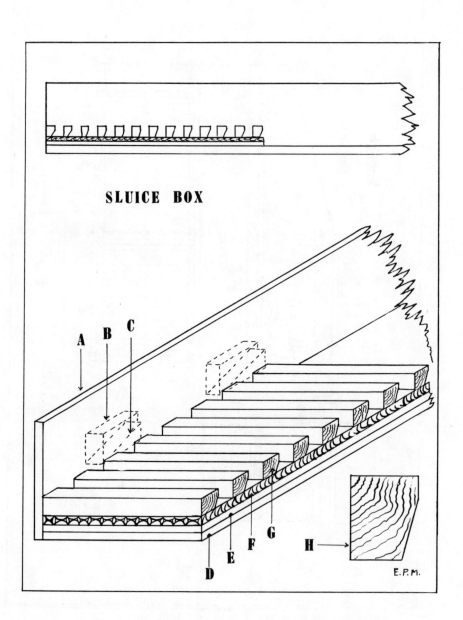

SLUICE BOX

SLUICE BOX PLANS AND DESCRIPTION

# Construction of A Sluicing Box

A. Sides. Clear, dry pine, straight grain, 3/4" stock, 8, 10, or 12" wide, 8, 10 or 12' long.

B. Wedge stops. Nail or screw to (A). Determine place and height when riffles, screen and carpeting are in place.

C. Wedges. Sometimes the wedges and wedge stops are cut from one piece of wood to get wedging effect, though many times a wedge 2" longer than wedge stop is better. If you cut the tapered end of the wedge blunt, it can be tapped out more easily.

D. Sluice box floor. Clear straight-grain dry wood the same length as the sides. This is determined by personal use. 3/4" stock 10, 12 or 14 inches wide. Screw and nail to sides water tight.

E. Carpeting. Burlap, blanketing or any suitable material to assist in holding GOLD. Cut same width as floor and same length as riffles.

F. Expanded metal or plaster screen cut same length as riffles and carpeting, and full width of floor. Be sure the steel angles head into the flow of water. This assists in creating a boiling action and forces the GOLD down into the carpeting.

G. Riffles. These vary with the width of the box. Usually one inch square with taper to create a boiling action.

H. Enlarged end view of riffle showing angle cut to create boiling action.

A small compact sluice box may be made as follows: Sides 3/4 in. x 8 in. x 8 ft. Use two boards. The floor, 3/4 in. x 12 in. x 8 ft. Riffles, 24 pieces 1 in. x 1 in. x 9-5/8 in. Two riffle guides 1 in. x 1 in. x 48 in. long (one on each side) to which each riffle is nailed (two nails each side) spaced one inch apart. Because boards are not always uniform in width, build your box then check inside space to which the riffles must fit and build to size. Allow for expansion of wood when wet. Use 2 in. wide cleats around each end to keep box rigid. Also large rocks set on top of these cleats help hold down sluice while working it, preventing it from floating off.

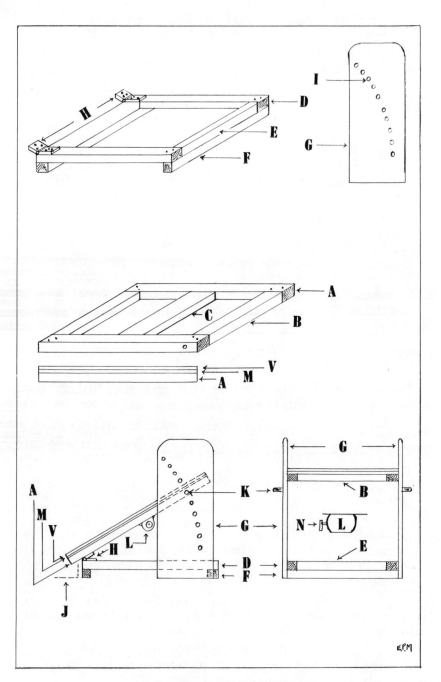

VIBRATOR PLANS

# Construction of A Vibrating Table

A. 2 pcs. 3/4 in. x 1 in. x 14 in. pine.
B. 2 pcs. 3/4 in. x 1 in. x 8 in. pine.
C. 1 pc. 3/4 in. x 2-1/4 in. x 8 in. pine.
D. 2 pcs. 3/4 in. x 1 in. x 12 in. pine.
E. 2 pcs. 3/4 in. x 3/4 in. x 8 in. pine.
F. 2 pcs. 3/4 in. x 3/4 in. x 10 in. pine.
G. 2 pcs. 1/4 in. x 5 in. x 14 in. plywood.
H. 2 hinges, pull pin type.
I. 10 holes, 1/4 in. diameter.
J. Cookie sheet or shallow pan.
K. 2 hardwood dowels 1/4 in. x 2 in.
L. Small motor.
M. 1 pc. 1/8 in. x 10 in. x 14 in. masonite
N. Motor weight vibrator.
V. 1 pc. 12 in. x 16 in. velvet (black).

Cut pieces, A, B and C to size. Glue and screw or nail together. Assemble frame. Next cut the piece of velvet (V). Black color is best. Tack lower end over frame. Pull tight across frame and tack or staple top end. No wrinkles. Take one side and tack, then pull tight and tack the other isde—again no wrinkles. Trim edges even.

Screw motor to center of block (C). Make (N) a thick steel washer. Drill off center then key or use allen screw to fasten to motor shaft. A small mechanical motor will do (some use small sewing machine motors or vibrating chair motors). Do not get too strong a motor or it will shake *everything* off. Some people do not even use a motor—just tap with their hand on top—but this is slow and tiresome.

Cut base frame pieces D, E, F. Glue and screw or nail frame together then mount and screw on hinges (H). Now stand vibrating table on end against hinges and screw hinges to back of table. Lower and check movement. Cut the plywood lever boards (G) and sand. Clamp to base frame. Check curve line for holes (I) by raising the table and marking curve with a pencil line. Remove and lay out holes. Drill both pieces together. Put in place and screw to base frame. Raise table and mark through hole with pencil on frame. Raise and lower to check alignment. Drill through (A) into (G) both sides. Place both dowels (K) into holes to hold table at the desired height.

Use a new grease-free cookie sheet for the pan (J). Place it under the end of the vibrating table. Follow instructions for recovering GOLD by vibrating table.

# GOLD SNIFFER

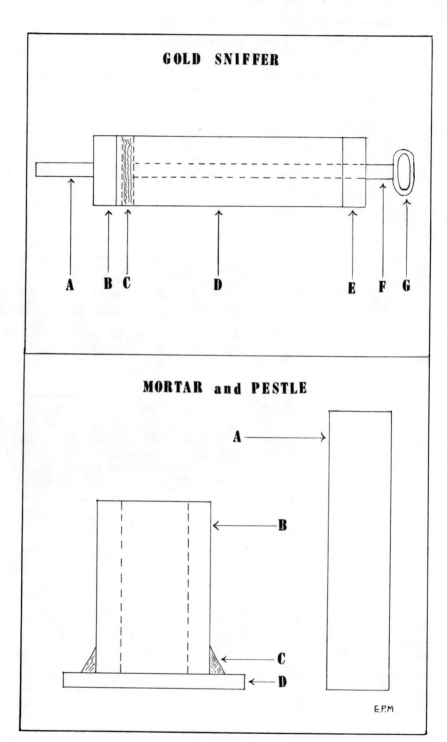

A    B C           D              E  F G

# MORTAR and PESTLE

A

B

C

D

E.P.M

# Construction of A Gold Sniffer

A. Snout or draw pipe. May be from 4 to 12 inches long. Thin wall pipe can be either welded or brazed to endcap. Slightly heavier pipe may be threaded 1/4 in. to 3/8 in. diameter.

B. Front cap. This should screw on or snap lock to make air tight. Diameter may range from 1-1/4 to 2 inches. Though somewhat heavy, this and the body (D) have been made of galvanized water pipe. Remodeling old auto air pumps has also worked. Cut off bottom and shorten the handle and snout. To empty the contents you have gathered, remove (B) and dump, then replace and continue sniffing.

C. Leather plunger. This should create a good suction. The more suction, the better the action. Drill hole in center for plunger bar. Use two large washers and two nuts, one on each side. The leather should form a cup with about 3/16 in. to 3/8 in. lip on the edge facing down toward (B). It must fit tight to walls (D). Lubricate leather with graphite or it will dry and lose its efficiency.

D. Tube body. May be thin-wall metal or heavy water pipe ranging from 1-1/4 to 2 inches in diameter and from 8 to 14 inches long.

E. Top cap. Same as (B). Should be removable to make replacement of (C) when necessary.

F. Pull rod or plunger. May be 1/4 to 3/8 inches diameter and long enough to extend past (E) 1-1/2 inches. Thread end for (C). Place on nut then steel washer. It should be 1/8 to 3/16 inches smaller than inside diameter of (D). The lower washer should fit into the leather cup on the bottom then place on the nut. Carefully place into tube and lubricate.

G. Handle grip of plunger bar. May be welded or brazed to (F), or

(F) can be heated and bent to form handle, all one piece.

The opening should allow room for fingers to get firm grip.

   This syringe-type sniffer can be made from a grease gun, providing there is absolutely no grease or you will coat the GOLD and lose it. The best type to use has both ends removable, especially the

## Construction of A Gold Sniffer

nozzle or front end, for cleaning out the GOLD. Of course, you can make a GOLD sniffer from many different materials. The secret is to have a draw-back type syringe suction. Have the nozzle long enough to enter narrow deep cracks. Water is necessary for good operation. The best method of operation is to keep the nozzle down while pulling back on the handle. Do not get too far back from the GOLD or you cannot pick it up. Guide the nozzle end always into the material and clean the very bottom as you move along. Dam dry cracks with mud and add water to keep suction operating unless you can pry open the crack and do crevicing. Wade into a stream and find natural cracks with GOLD. Good spots can have more GOLD next year, so keep notes on good finds.

## Construction of A Mortar and Pestle

A. Pestle or plunger. The length and diameter of (A) is determined by the size of (B). The plunger is driven down with sufficient force to crush the material under it when placed inside of (B).

B. Mortar. A container for material to be crushed. Thick wall pipe works fine. Length and diameter is determined by the amount and size of material to be crushed.

C. Weld all around to marry (B) to (D).

D. Base plate or steel or iron. Cut round larger than (B) with enough room to weld. Be sure (B) and (D) fit flat together. You may have to lathe turn (B) to assure a flat surface.

### Recommended Equipment for the Week End Amateur Prospector

1. A GOLD pan.
2. Pick and shovel. Also small miners or prospector's pick.
3. Container for GOLD. If possible, non-breakable, with large mouth and screw on cap or lid.
4. Magnifying glass. Folding type preferred for protection.
5. Sharp pocket knife. May have magnetic blade—or separate magnet.
6. First aid kit. Snake bite kit also.
7. Canteen of drinking water and a few dry food rations. Even if you are going out for only a few hours, some people do get lost, and food and water may mean survival.

Other equipment will depend on where you are going and what you intend to do and where. Maybe you will need a rocker or sluice, etc. If you are mining near your car you may use a galvanized tub to wash your equipment and bring back your collection of sand and GOLD to clean up in spare time at home.

# Rebellious Ore of Meadow Lake

In the Nevada County Meadow Lake area is located on timber-covered slopes of the western side of the Sierra Nevadas rich deposits known as "rebellious GOLD." Here early pioneers built the town of Meadow Lake in 1865. It was incorporated in 1866, then all but abandoned by late 1872. When a population of several thousands occupied the town in its hey-day it contained thirteen hotels, two theaters, a weekly newspaper, and bank and stock exchange, and of course a brewery. It too had a church and a large number of stores, saloons and dives found in all early type mining camps and towns. Today the metropolis is but a memory (beyond even being called a ghost town) for all that remains is rotted lumber and a few cabins built at a later date. Yet the ore on and in the ground remains as rich as ever—just rebellious.

You reach the location by auto from Truckee via Webber Lake at an altitude over 7200 feet. On the surface that has decomposed, much free GOLD has occurred but it was soon replaced by sulphides mixed with fine GOLD, beginning the concentration known as "rebellious GOLD." Within this conglomerate mixture are found pyrite (an abundant sulphide) with arsenical and cupriferous sulphides, lead and zinc sulphide, and some galena.

Different milling processes have been attempted yet all have defeated the efforts of the pioneer miners. Of course in this early day of mining at Meadow Lake, the metallurgical knowledge was quite limited. Too, modern machinery was not available, nor good road building equipment. The stage route in was rough. Today's roads are much better. Even with early processing methods, great loss in their tailings, and cheap labor, some made a good living.

Someone today with new knowledge, ideas and finance might look into the area. Thousands of tons of ore lay piled ready to be milled—deserted when the area folded up in 1870. Also thousands of tons of tailings, partially processed or poorly processed still remain over the countryside. Some areas produced ore that brought $2.50 per pound, while others were assayed $411.50 per ton. In 1901 it is alleged that GOLD in the amount of $1000 in a single pan of ore occurred in one small pocket. Actual proof, however, has not been produced to say it actually went that high. It's possible. Some specimens recovered around 1936 have run as high as $25 a pound.

Here is an example of one rebellious GOLD area—and there are others—defying and challenging man to scientifically create a better way to process and separate that precious metal, GOLD, from its bounds of rebellious minerals (sulphides).

# Famous Gold Nuggets

1. The "Welcome Stranger" is the world's largest nugget found or recorded. It was discovered in the rut of a dirt road made by the wheels of carts that traveled the road, only a couple of inches beneath the surface. Found near Moliagul, Victoria, Australia, February 5, 1869, the "Welcome Stranger" weighed 2,516 troy ounces and was valued at $46,428. It took several men to carry it. A facsimile can be seen at the San Francisco Ferry Building in the California Division of Mines. Museum Item No. 20969.

2. "Carson Hill," found November 22, 1854, weight, 2,340 troy oz. or 195 lbs., valued at $77,200. The Morgan stope on the Morgan claim was operated by steam shovels on the surface, but from the tunnels below most of the ore was removed. This nugget was so large (54 inches high and 5-1/2 inches thick) it had to be cut into four parts, and each piece was a full load for the four men that carried it out. The California mother lode surrendered a real prize!

3. The "Welcome Nugget" was Australia's first surprise, found 180 feet underground in a GOLD mine at Bakery Hill, Ballarat, Victoria, Australia, weight 2,195 troy oz., valued at $45,320. Facsimile No. 2920 at the Ferry Building.

4. The "Monumental Mine" nugget was found in the Sierra City district near Downieville in 1869. It weighed 1898 troy oz.

5. "Blanch Barkley" was a south Australian nugget weighing 1752 troy oz.

6. Another "Monumental" nugget (1,596 troy oz.) was found in 1860 near Sierra City, California.

7. "Knapp's Ranch" nugget, found in 1850 at Columbia, weighed 1000 troy oz.

8. "Woods Creek" nugget found in 1848 in the Sonora district of California weighed 75 lbs. or 900 troy oz.

9. The much written about "Dog Town Nugget" was found in 1859 and weighed 648 troy oz. or 54 lbs.

10. The "Pilot Hill" nugget, 425 troy oz., was found in 1867 in El Dorado County, California.

11. The "GOLD Hill" nugget was found in 1850 near Columbia, California. It weighed 360 troy oz.

12. The "Downieville" nugget, found in 1850 weighed 300 troy oz. (25 lbs.)

Do not get the impression all nuggets are buried deep within the earth, for many (both large and small) are found right on the surface and in or near stream beds. Yes, it would be nice and thrilling to find your own nugget. They could be found right where you are walking, so be alert to the things and world around you. It pays off better and more often than you may realize.

# Gold Strikes

A remarkable story was published in the April 1964 issue of "California Mining Journal." Part of it is quoted here:

Imagine the thrill of striking a rich GOLD-bearing ancient channel while digging a hole for a septic tank in preparation of developing a lode mine. This is exactly what happened to J. E. and C. C. Chapin at their Mary Hazel Mine in Trinity County.

Actually the Chapins had proved a sufficient discovery of GOLD located under an iron cap to qualify them for an O.M.E. loan. Preparing to develop the known ore bodies they decided to install a septic tank for their sanitary facilities. While digging the hole, they struck an ancient channel which was hidden under the over-burden. Previously they thought this ancient channel ran off their property and were unaware that the channel had made a turn and came back across their property.

Mrs. Chapin, who prefers to be called "Jane," will not divulge exactly how much GOLD she dug from this hole, but she assures us that it was more than enough to purchase a new 1964 pick-up truck. The GOLD was tarnished, and at first they almost threw it away thinking the GOLD was iron nuggets. Upon further testing, however, they discovered it was pure GOLD. Out of one pan of gravel they recovered $162.70 worth of GOLD as weighed on a hand scale, and according to Jane some pans ran richer than this.

At the present time development work is proceeding on other nearby claims. Their property was located years ago—they came to that area in 1932 and they scratched at the claims throughout the depression, panning enough GOLD to keep things together and make payments on the claims. "If we panned a dollar's worth of dust, we ate a dollar's worth of food," Jane recalls.

Jane Chapin has fought long and hard for a raise in the price of GOLD and a decent break for the miners. A sore spot with her is the present interpretation of the mining laws wherein the Bureau of Land Management requires the discovery hole to always be available for their inspection. "I think I've got the answer to that one!" Jane said with a twinkle in her eye. "Instead of going ahead with our septic tank, we have decided to build an appropriate building with the proper moon-shaped crest on the door and with the necessary peekholes inside. Then," she went on to say with tongue in cheek, "when one of these bureaucrats shows up to inspect our discovery hole, they can open the door and look down the hole." Wouldn't that be the most unique discovery monument in the West?

# Gold Strikes

The Chapins displayed their GOLD in 1965 at the California State Fair and I made it a point to talk to them. Jane said she would like to take all kids out and show them how to pan for GOLD so there wouldn't be so much juvenile delinquency. She further said, "and if we could just teach the older folks how to pan and hunt for rocks, why they wouldn't have such lonely lives." The one big dream of this couple is to do something about a subsidy for GOLD miners. Nothing really seems impossible after you find a small fortune in GOLD while digging for a septic tank.

\* \* \*

About August 1, 1965, a 10½ oz. GOLD nugget was found near Downieville, said to be valued at $1000. This was on a rocky section of an unpaved road. Nuggets often are worth more than their GOLD weight value.

\* \* \*

# Fisherman Story

A trout fisherman was having bad luck in fishing so he decided maybe a different bait was needed. "I think I'll try finding some Hellgrammites." Walking along the stream, he began to turn over some rocks at the water's edge. In turning over one large rock, he saw something shiny. Removing his hat, he scooped with both hands the wet sand, small gravel and colored grains into his hat; collected his fishing gear; returned to his car and drove off. He was interested in his find so he thought he would stop at a small mountain town and visit a rock shop he had seen on another trip. When the rock hound saw the nuggets, he told the fisherman indeed it was GOLD.

The fisherman asked if the rock hound store owner knew how to pan what he had in his hat. "No," was the answer, "but around the corner lives an old man that has done lots of panning. Go and see him." This the fisherman did, and the old man panned out the GOLD, revealing quite a large amount. He said, "Son, this is a good haul. You had better check around for some more." The fisherman asked if he could pay to learn how to pan, and before the day was through he had learned to pan and was ready to go back and look for more GOLD. He was started on a new adventure. Soon he was spending more time panning for GOLD than fishing. In fact, the only time he wet a trout fly was when he thought a fresh fried trout would taste good, but panning for GOLD became a fascinating and profitable hobby.

# Gold History

When early prehistoric man arrived, probably the first metal to attract his attention was GOLD, but he had to wait until the Bronze Age to learn the art of melting. The earliest mining work of which traces remain was on GOLD ores in Egypt, and GOLD washing is depicted on monuments of the Fourth Dynasty showing slave miners engaged in placer mining auriferous sands in hollowed out stone basins (early GOLD pans) and melting the GOLD in primitive furnaces by means of mouth blow pipes.

Later, in the year 1200 B.C., the legend of the "GOLDEN Fleece" tells of a greedy expedition led by the Greek, Jason, to capture GOLD from Armenia. His ship, "Argos," gave us the name "Argonauts," or GOLD Seekers. This GOLD was collected by slaves who laboriously washed the GOLD from the river gravels with the aid of sheepskins, thus the "GOLDEN Fleece."

Coming to the Birth of Christ, GOLD was the Christmas present of the first Wise Man, Melchior.

The history of GOLD in California began in the year 1510 when a Spanish novel, "Las Sergas de Esplandian" by G. O. Montalvo was published in Toledo, Spain. It was purely a fictional novel which told about an island called "California" which was peopled with black women, and the only metal was pure GOLD. Even though it was a fictional place, yet undiscovered, a great many people set out to find the rich island, among them Cortes, Balboa and Coronado.

Soon other tales, or rumors, started, telling of the Seven Cities of Cibola, followed by the kingdom of La Gran Quivira, and the GOLD hoard called "El Dorado." All added fuel to the fire. Later a missionary solved the tale of the Seven Golden Cities of Cibola. They were Indian adobe houses that showed GOLDEN color in the sunset. On July 2, 1542, Juan R. Cabrillo first officially recorded the name "California" in his log while off the tip of lower California. He thought he had found the rich island named in the book 32 years before.

# Gold History

The first knowledge of GOLD in California was the GOLD nuggets brought to the Mission Padres by the native Indians. Later the Padres gave some of the GOLD to the soldiers for pay. Then two California men reported finds. First, in 1841, a Canadian, Jean Baptiste Reuelle, made public a find in the mountains about 30 miles northeast of San Fernando Mission. Second, a native Californian, Francisco Lopez, made a discovery at San Francisquito Canyon, about 35 miles northwest of Los Angeles. In March 1842 Lopez, with a companion, was searching for some stray horses. About noon they stopped under some trees and while resting in the shade, Lopez took his knife and dug up some wild onions. He found small GOLD nuggets clinging to the roots. Soon his report started a small GOLD rush. On November 22, 1842, an American trader, Abel Stearns, sent 18-3/4 oz. of GOLD from San Francisquito Canyon to Alfred Robinson to take to the Philadelphia Mint for assay. But the world had to wait six more years before the great GOLD rush of '49.

The GOLD rush of 1849 started the greatest decade of change in California from 1849 to 1859. It all started on January 24, 1848, when James W. Marshall discovered GOLD in the tailrace of Capt. Sutter's Coloma sawmill. And this little discovery received worldwide attention, mainly through the efforts of Sam Brannan, a Mormon newspaperman in San Francisco, merchant and general promoter. The miners poured into the Mother Lode area. They first used bateas, GOLD pans, and every bowl, tray and warming pan available.

The years 1850-1861, inclusive, showed very good GOLD production. In fact, never did it fall below 41 million dollars in annual production. The year 1852 proved a boom, when the annual amount produced was $81,294,700. Then, beginning in 1863 until the end of World War 1 in 1918, the annual output averaged around 16 to 17 million dollars. Beginning in 1918, increased production costs in GOLD mining began to cut annual production. By now, most GOLD mining was done in tunnels and shafts, operated by large mining companies rather than the thousands of lone miners and prospectors that had worked surface or placer GOLD up to the 1880's. Thus by 1929 the annual production reached a low of $8,526,703. Many people were feeling the pinch of unemployment and, in general, affairs were in a sad state economically.

A worldwide economic crisis developed, soon followed by the great depression of 1929. When the U. S. stock market crash came, the death rate took a sudden leap. Those who had been millionaires the day before were broke and penniless, leading to many suicides. Panic struck across the nation, and prices and market values dropped to rock bottom. With the bread lines forming and hunger prevailing, the state of affairs for everyone was shattered.

# Gold History

Then, in the depression of 1930, began the next movement to the old GOLD fields. The *new* GOLD rush was on. Taking the few personal possessions they had, people walked, rode, drove and used every form of available transportation. Family groups and single men all headed into the hills and mountains, for here GOLD had once saved the lives of the poor, and it could do it again. With high hopes and determination to succeed they followed practically the same procedure that the early argonauts of 1849 had used.

The familiar scenes along the same streams and gulches where ghost towns stood, again began to return to life—though not as in the rip-roaring hey-day of the 1849's. A more serious state of mind existed, very careful searching and even the smallest of GOLD dust was saved. Painstakingly slow at first, every grain was watched, washed and recovered, for the money this GOLD brought now was sorely needed. Once again tent cities sprang up on many of the same spots previously used by the 49'ers. This new generation of young and old, professional and amateur GOLD miners lived and worked side by side. Women and children labored with blistered hands and aching backs beside their loved ones. With meager meals and long hours of hard work, the few hours of rest at night were their greatest blessing.

For years the price of GOLD was valued at $20.67 per ounce. In the year 1933, after August 12, it was possible to sell GOLD on the world open market from $29.25 per ounce to $34.00 per ounce by the end of that year. Then on January 31, 1934, the United States official Mint price was set at $35.00 an ounce.

With the increased activity in GOLD mining, the flow of GOLD was on the increase continually since 1927, and statistics published by the California Division of Mines gave the following table for this State's GOLD production:

| Year | Value |
|------|-------|
| 1929 | $ 8,526,703 |
| 1930 | 9,451,162 |
| 1931 | 10,841,162 |
| 1932 | 11,765,726 |
| 1933 | 14,217,600 |

# Gold History

This was encouraging to the desperate people that had ventured into California GOLD fields to eke out an existence. Many had made a fair success of it and the economy had leveled off somewhat. Practically every method and means employed in the 1849-1870 era was used, as well as new inventions.

Data gathered and published by the California Division of Mines showed that in 1932 between 12,000 and 15,000 persons engaged in this work during the year, recovered a total of $500,000 in GOLD during an average working period of 100 days.

While it is true that the individual's return then was small, and in many cases averaged less than 50 cents a day per person, prices on food and necessities were low too. Also, many found that this vigorous type of living with hard work and long hours in the fresh air and sunshine was a healthier life than that of the crowded cities. Here, even though they were just getting by, some were making good progress and enjoying it as well. A new breed of human beings were again formulating a changing pattern of life— a retraining period.

Today the GOLD is still there, and for a week end family outing in the fresh air, prospecting can be exciting and fun.

# Definitions

ALLUVIAL FAN—Soil washed or drifted down from mountains forming a tapered fan-shaped slope out into the valley.

ALLUVIUM—The soil that forms the alluvial fan.

AMALGAM—Mercury (Hg) mixed with GOLD, silver, copper or other metals. Usually a soft mass.

AMALGAMATION—A process in which Mercury is used to collect and hold GOLD.

APRON—The canvas or cloth part of a rocker used to catch and hold GOLD.

ARGONAUTS—GOLD seekers (from the ship ARGOS in Greek mythology).

ARRASTRA—Early type rock crusher. Also called a drag mill.

ASSAY—Test of the goodness, purity, weight, value, etc. of metals.

AURIFEROUS—(A-RIF'ER-US)—Sands and gravel containing GOLD.

BAJADAS—Spanish for desert alluvial fans.

BATEA—Early type wooden GOLD pan.

BEDROCK—The solid layer of rock below the earth's surface.

BENCH—Exposed cut in ancient river bed.

BLACK SAND—A mixture of heavy, dark minerals and metals.

CARAT—24 Carat GOLD is 100% pure.

CINNABAR—The red rock body of Mercury not yet processed.

COLOR—The term given very small particles of visible GOLD.

CRADLE or ROCKER—An early device used to recover GOLD.

CREVICES—Cracks and breaks, usually in bedrock.

CRUST—The upper surface of the earth.

CRYSTALS—Formation of minerals that helps determine their contents.

DREDGER—A mechanical device to bring GOLD-bearing materials up from water for recovery.

DUST—Very fine ground GOLD, powdery.

EL ORO—Spanish for GOLD.

EUREKA—A term used by early miners meaning "I have found it."

# Definitions

FLAKE GOLD—Heavy pieces of GOLD, smaller than nuggets.

FLOUR GOLD—Otherwise known as GOLD dust.

FOOL'S GOLD—Pyrite or iron pyrite. Golden yellow color, brittle.

FREE GOLD—Small particles of native GOLD.

GEM STONES—Semi-precious stones hard enough to cut and polish.

GOLD—A precious metal of bright yellow color. The most ductile and malleable of all metals and one of the heaviest.

GOLD NUGGETS—GOLD particles not passing through a 10 mesh screen.

GOLD PAN—Heavy metal pan specially designed to assist in GOLD recovery.

GOLD SNIFFER—Suction syringe type instrument used to suck GOLD from crevices.

GRADING PLATE—Steel plate punctured to grade the size of gravels.

GRAIN—Same as flakes of GOLD. 24 grains of GOLD equals 1 penny weight (troy).

GRIZZLY—A box using a grading plate or screen.

HEADER—Leading box, trough, or sluice. The top or head end. Same as "Grizzly."

JIG—A mechanical device to further the recovery of GOLD. Example: Vibrating concentrating tables.

LAVA—Molten magma leaving a volcano.

LODE—A metallic or mineral vein such as the "Mother Lode" GOLD vein.

MAGMA—A pasty mixture of molten minerals within the earth.

MERCURY—Element (Hg). Used in the recovery of GOLD by amalgamation.

NATURAL RIFFLES—Small steps or ledges in bedrock. Depressions holding GOLD.

PLACER—A gravelly place where FREE GOLD is found.

PLATINUM—A metal of white color like silver, but of inferior luster. It is the heaviest of known metals.

# Definitions

PYRITE—"Fools' GOLD." (FeS2) Brassy yellow. Sulphide of Iron. Brittle.

QUARTZ—Forms about 12% of the rocks of the earth's crust. Vein-quartz, in many cases contains GOLD. Composed of silica and oxygen.

QUATERNARY—(Kwa-ter'na-ri) Fourth period of time, from present back to the end of the tertiary period.

QUICKSILVER—Another name for Mercury.

RESIDUAL PLACER—GOLD and decomposed rock are left in approximately their original location.

RETORT—Process of recovering GOLD from Mercury by heating in a retorer.

RIFFLES—Obstructions to hold GOLD and heavy metals in rocker, sluice box and long tom.

SAMPLING—Panning test areas prior to larger operation.

SCUBA—Self-contained underwater breathing apparatus.

SLUICE BOX—Trough constructed to catch GOLD from soil and gravel, while washed with a current of running water.

SPARK ARRESTOR—Metal container on gasoline engine to prevent sparks from starting fires.

SUCTION DREDGE—Dredging operation sucking up materials for GOLD processing.

TAILINGS—Sands and gravels left after mining process is complete.

TERTIARY—(Ter'-shi-a-ri) Third period of time, in which transported GOLD and auriferous sands and gravels became placers.

TRESPASSING—Entering upon private property without permission.

VEIN—Surface cracks or fissures, filled with GOLD, usually called a Lode.

WINNOWING—Method of dry placer mining by using air.

# Weights and Measures

## Troy Weight

24 grains ........................................................... 1 pennyweight

20 pennyweights ................................................. 1 ounce

12 ounces ........................................................ 1 pound

## Equivalents

1 ounce troy *equals* 1.097 ounce avoirdupois *equals* 31.103 grams

1 ounce avoirdupois *equals* 0.911 ounce troy *equals* 28.35 grams

1 pound troy *equals* 0.8229 pound avoirdupois *equals* 13.166 ozs. avoirdupois *equals* 373.2 grams

1 pound avoirdupois *equals* 1.215 pounds troy *equals* 14.58 ounces troy *equals* 453.6 grams

✗ 23

The following table is based upon NEW coins only; gold at $35 per oz.

| | Weight | | Value of Equal Weight of Gold | | | |
| Coin | Grains | Pennyweights | 1000 fine | 900 fine | 800 fine | 700 fine |
|---|---|---|---|---|---|---|
| Copper cent | 48.000 | 2.000 | $ 3.50 | $ 3.15 | $ 2.80 | $ 2.45 |
| Nickel | 77.160 | 3.215 | 5.63 | 5.06 | 4.50 | 3.94 |
| Dime | 38.581 | 1.608 | 2.81 | 2.53 | 2.25 | 1.97 |
| Quarter | 96.452 | 4.019 | 7.03 | 6.33 | 5.63 | 4.92 |
| Half dollar | 192.904 | 8.038 | 14.07 | 12.66 | 11.25 | 9.85 |
| Silver dollar | 412.500 | 17.188 | 30.08 | 27.07 | 24.06 | 21.06 |

The average fineness of all placer gold mined in Nevada between 1906 and 1934 was approximately 713.

# Recommended Reading

Zim, Shaffer and Pearlman. 1957, *Rocks and Minerals;* Simon and Schuster, 159 pp.

Averill, Charles V., 1946, *Placer mining for gold in California:* California Div. of Mines Bul. 135, 477 pp.

Boericke, William F., 1941, *Prospecting and operating small gold placers:* John Wiley and sons, Inc.

Clark, William B., 1957, *Gold:* California Div. Mines Bull. **176,** pp. 215-226.

Clark, William B., 1960, *Skin diving for gold in California:* Mineral Information Service, vol. 13, no. 6, 8 pp.

Dorr, John V. N., and Bosqui, F. L., 1950, *Cyanidation and concentration of gold and silver ores,* 2nd ed., McGraw Hill Book Co., 500 pp.

Douglas, Jack, 1948, *Gold in placer;* published by Jack Douglas, Box 165, Dutch Flat, California, 123 pp.

Gardner, E. D. and Johnson, C. H., 1934, *Placer mining in the western United States;* U. S. Bur. Mines Information Circulars 6786, 6787, and 6788.

Gardner, D. L., 1954, *Gold and silver mining districts in the Mojave desert region of Southern California:* California Div. Mines Bull. 170, Chap. 8, no. 6, pp. 51-58.

Gilmore, C. L., and Stewart, R. M., 1962, *Legal guide for California prospectors and miners:* California Div. Mines and Geology.

Hulin, Carlton D., 1925, *Geology and ore deposits of the Randsburg quadrangle, California:* California Min. Bur. Bull. 95, 152 pp.

Jenkins, Olaf P., and others, 1948, *Geologic guidebook along Highway 49—Sierran gold belt—the Mother Lode Country:* California Div. Mines Bull. 141, 221 pp.

Laizure, C. McK., 1932, *Elementary placer mining methods and gold-saving devices:* Calif. Div. Mines Rept. 28, pp. 112-204.

Lindgren, Waldemar, 1911, *The Tertiary gravels of the Sierra Nevada of California:* U. S. Geol. Survey Prof. Paper 73, 226 pp.

Logan, C. A., 1935, *Mother Lode gold belt of California:* California Div. Mines Bull. 108, 240 pp.

Logan, Clarence A., 1936, *Gold mines of Placer County:* California Div. Mines Rept. 32, pp. 7-96.

Pages of History, 1960, *Diving and digging for gold,* Sausalito, California, Pages of History (Box 6).

von Bernewitz, M. W., 1943, *Handbook for prospectors and operators of small mines,* 4th ed., McGraw-Hill Book Company, 547 pp.

Bradley, Walter W., State Mineralogist, 1934: *California Journal of Mines and Geology.*

Thompson and West, 1880, *Histry of Nevada County, California.* (Story on "rebellious gold".)

# Plans and Materials
(Prices include all taxes and postage)

Gold Pans

12 inch $4.00
16 inch $5.50

These are steel pans with rolled wire reinforced rims.

Plans—

| | |
|---|---|
| Sluice box | $3.00 |
| Vibrating table | $3.00 |
| Mortar and Pestle | $2.00 |
| Long Tom | $3.50 |
| Gold Rocker knockdown | $3.00 |

Miniature Models—

| | |
|---|---|
| Sluice box 10½ inches long | $4.50 |
| Gold Rocker 8 inches long | $4.50 |

Each of native wood with an interesting printed story free with purchase.

Western Golden state jewelry—
Bolo ties—Bracelets—Pendants—Earrings—Cuff link and tie bar sets. Hand made with 23 karat hammered gold embedments. Prices ranging from $3.00—$10.00. Write for information.

Actual size sluice boxes, Gold rockers and Long Toms may be purchased already constructed in case you don't want to build your own. Send for price list.

Any one with any questions on California Gold Findings or California History. Please write me. Send self-addressed stamped envelope. All letters will be answered as soon as possible. Thank you.

THE OLD PROSPECTOR
Edwin P. Morgan
P. O. Box 20094
Sacramento, Calif. 95820

# Golden Notes